# THE MAN
# WHO CARED

# The Man Who Cared

## A LIFE OF

# HARRY S TRUMAN

*Victor Wolfson*

ARIEL BOOKS

FARRAR, STRAUS AND GIROUX

Mr. Truman inscribed his book *Mr. Citizen* to my young son in these words:

"For Tom. I hope he has a good life."

This present book is dedicated to all *my* young friends. I hope *they* have a good life.

I wish to thank Mr. Truman, Mr. David Niles, and Mr. Ben Gradus for the use of material and statements never before used in print, from the television series *Decision: The Conflicts of Harry S Truman,* produced by Ben Gradus and distributed by Screen Gems, Inc.

I also am grateful to Mr. Alfred Steinberg, whose book *The Man from Missouri* is filled with excellent political material.

Margaret Truman's book *Souvenir* afforded me many insights into the personal behavior of Mr. Truman. And Mr. Jonathan Daniels's book *The Man of Independence* was a rewarding experience.

To Mrs. Arlene Kraat, my sincerest thanks and admiration. She was able to type this volume from my practically illegible handwritten manuscript.

Victor Wolfson

Warwick, New York
June 1965

# Part One

# 1

A little old lady sat in the kitchen of her Missouri farmhouse reading a letter addressed to herself and to her daughter.

"Dear Mama and Mary," the letter said, "I am getting ready to see Stalin, and Churchill, and it is a chore. I have to take my tuxedo, tails, preacher coat, high hat, low hat and hard hat as well as sundry other things. Wish I didn't have to go, but I do— Hope you are well. I sent a check today.

"Love—
*Harry*"

Harry was the little old lady's son and he happened to be the President of the United States of America.

He hadn't been President very long; less than three months, in fact. It came about this way. The date was April 12, 1945. At about twenty minutes after five that afternoon Harry S Truman, who had been elected Vice-President, was in the Senate Office Building in Washington, D.C., when he received a telephone call. He was to come swiftly and secretly to the White House. When he arrived, he was immediately brought upstairs to the second-floor study of Eleanor Roosevelt. Mrs. Roosevelt greeted him and, putting her arm around his shoulder, said quietly, "Harry, the President is dead."

Harry Truman remembered later that he felt as though a ton of hay had just fallen on him. He fought off tears.

"The lightning had struck. America had lost a great leader, and I was faced with a terrible responsibility."

The United States was in the throes of the greatest war the world had ever known. The Germans were being defeated in Europe, but still they fought ferociously. And in the Far East, the Japanese were being pushed back to their home islands, but they fought the Allies like demons, inflicting heavy losses.

Now Harry S Truman was about to assume the role of Commander-in-Chief of the Armed Forces of the United States. He would become the Chief of this enormous and powerful fighting force as soon as he took the oath of office. It was a terrible moment for the slight, nearsighted man, who had not been permitted to share one of the great secrets of the war, who had not been permitted to concern himself

4

overmuch with the strategy of the war. Now, suddenly, it would be he who would take charge.

A certain confusion reigned in the White House. No one could find a Bible on which the Vice-President could take his oath. Too, Harry wanted his wife Bess and his daughter Margaret to be present at this, the most important moment of his life. They had to be summoned to the White House.

They were at the small apartment that the Trumans called home during their stay in Washington. At that moment on April, 12, Margaret was rushing about the apartment getting dressed for a gay dinner party. She was twenty-one and she had bought a new dress for the party and she had a new beau. The telephone rang. She picked up the receiver and heard her father's crisp voice.

"Hi, Dad," she greeted him pertly.

"Let me speak to your mother," he said. His voice sounded tight and funny, Margaret thought.

"Are you coming home to dinner?" Margaret asked. "I'm going out to a dinner party."

"Let me speak to your mother," her father repeated sternly.

"I only asked you a civil question," his daughter pouted into the phone.

"Margaret, will you let me speak to your mother?"

"Mother!" Margaret called, turning toward the living room of the apartment.

When Bess Truman hung up after speaking to her husband on the telephone, tears were running down her cheeks.

"Mother," Margaret cried, "what's the matter? What is it?"

"President Roosevelt is dead," Mrs. Truman said. Glancing at the party dress her daughter wore, she added: "You had better change your clothes." Margaret left the room. She telephoned her new beau and called off their date. Then she changed her clothes.

"It hadn't occurred to me," Margaret confesses, "that Daddy was about to become President of the United States."

A Secret Service car had been dispatched to the apartment house. Bess Truman and her daughter got in and were driven off to the White House.

A half hour later, in the Cabinet Room, Harry S Truman, who had been a farm boy in Missouri, was sworn in as the thirty-third President of the United States.

After the brief ceremony, Bess Truman and Margaret left the White House and returned to their modest apartment. A little while later, Harry came in. He seemed stunned, almost in a state of shock. He ate a ham sandwich and drank a glass of milk. That was the first dinner he had as President of the United States.

Twenty years later, someone asked Harry Truman what his happiest day in the White House had been.

"The day I left it," he said.

Independence, Missouri, where the new President had lived most of his life, lies about ten miles south of Kansas City. The city has a small public square surrounding the courthouse. It also has a public library and several small banks. All these places played a role in the life of the young man who was destined one day to become President of the United States. In years past, from 1831 to 1844, Independence was the starting place for the wagon trains that set out over the Santa Fe and Oregon trails to make the long, hazardous journey to the Far West. In Independence these wagon trains were outfitted not only with provisions for the trek but with guns with which to fight off the Indians. Independence, Missouri, was the jumping-off place for the new frontier, and some of this adventurous spirit overlay the solid, sturdy, small-town atmosphere of the city of Truman's boyhood days. And some of this quality must have been bred into the boy who was raised there. A small town in coastal New England, say, had quite a different atmosphere. It was the sense of the sea, of the rocky soil, and the elements of culture in an old and settled society which influenced and molded the men of New England.

But in Independence, Missouri, the doorway to the Far West, surrounded by fertile, agricultural communities, different influences were exerted on the inhabitants, and they resulted in the making of a different kind of man.

Harry S Truman was born in a little house in the village of Lamar, Missouri, on May 8, 1884. Lamar, besides having the honor of being the birthplace of the thirty-third President of the United States, also has the dubious distinction of being the birthplace of the notorious outlaw Jesse James.

Later, when Truman was in politics, he spoke of Jesse

7

James with a certain boyish admiration. Truman was attacking the railroad barons who were robbing investors of millions of dollars. He said, "Speaking of Rock Island reminds me that the first railroad robbery was committed on the Rock Island in 1873, just east of Council Bluffs, Iowa. The man who committed *that* robbery used a gun and a horse, and got up early in the morning." (Getting up early in the morning had always been a virtue with Harry Truman.) "He and his gang," he continued, "took a chance of being killed, and eventually all of them *were* killed. The loot was three thousand dollars. That railroad robber's name was Jesse James. About thirty years after the Council Bluffs hold-up, the Rock Island went through a looting by some gentlemen known as the tin-plate millionaires. *They* used no guns, but they ruined a railroad and got away with seventy million dollars or more. They did it by means of holding companies. Senators can see what 'pikers' Jesse James and his crowd were alongside of some real artists."

Truman's birthplace was on frontier farming land, where memories of frontier life were still fresh. He was indeed born and bred at the crossroads of America.

As a boy he wasn't strong. Diphtheria left him paralyzed for a time, and his eyes were weak. Before he was nine, he began to wear eyeglasses, which at the time in Missouri were meant to be worn only by old people. This early wearing of eyeglasses had an effect on the character of young Harry Truman. He turned away from the rough games usually played by nine-year-old boys. He turned to books and read everything in sight. And he became something of a mama's boy. Not that he was ever a sissy, but he hung around his mother and helped her in the kitchen. He seemed to enjoy it. At an early age he learned to cook and to play the piano. It is reported that as a boy he learned to arrange his sister Mary Jane's hair as expertly as his mother did.

But for all this withdrawal from the ordinary rough play of boys his age there were compensations. His nearsightedness had removed him from a boyish world of physical action. But it increased his yearning for a life of action in other fields. Years later, politics was to be the activity in which the handicapped Truman would express himself with vigor and toughness.

In those early years, however, like many other boys, Harry Truman had no idea what he wanted to be or do in life. His mother had given him piano lessons and thought perhaps he would become a musician. When he was about thirteen, he began to study the piano seriously.

The Trumans at that time lived on Waldo Street in Independence. Next door lived Miss Florence Burrus, who gave him his first formal instruction in the art of playing the piano. Later he studied with Mrs. E. C. White.

"She was a wonderful woman and a fine teacher," Truman has said. "I wanted to be a musician and she encouraged me. I would get up every morning and practice for two hours, and twice a week I went to Mrs. White."

It required a certain spunk (which never left him) to

9

ignore the jeers of his friends and go to his music teacher twice a week, carrying his music roll.

On his first day in Sunday School, he saw for the first time Elizabeth Virginia Wallace, or "Bess," as she was called. "I was too backward to look at her very much," Truman remembered. "And I didn't speak to her for five years." It was Bess Wallace who would one day become his wife.

Truman's father John had been a farmer, working the 200-acre family farm at Grandview some twenty miles from Independence. When John Truman quit the farm, he became a mule trader.

"He was the kind of man," his son Harry said, "who could tell a mule's age by a glance and did not have to examine his teeth." But John Truman did not favor his son Harry. His affections went to Harry's brother Vivian, a rugged lad with a love for the outdoors. When Vivian was not yet in his teens, John Truman took him into the mule-swapping business; they were partners and fast friends. But Harry admired his scrappy father, who was always getting into fights over politics; John Truman must have had a strong influence on the boy's character. If Harry, at the time, was not a rugged, outdoor, fighting Truman, he was the reader of the family. He would disappear for hours into the quiet of the Independence Public Library.

"I read everything I could get my hands on," he said, "—histories and encyclopedias and everything else." And he read the Bible. He had read it twice by the time he was twelve.

When he was sixteen, Harry S Truman had his first close brush with politics. In 1900 the Democrats held their national convention in Kansas City, not far from Independence. Harry, helped by his father, got a job as a page boy at the convention.

"I remember that there were seventeen thousand people in the old convention hall," Truman said, "and when William Jennings Bryan spoke, his appeal that day was like nothing I have ever heard. He had a bell-like voice that carried well and he knew how to use it."

Harry also had a job in Jim Clinton's Drugstore on the square in Independence. He reported for work at six-thirty in the morning, and worked until it was time to set out for high school. He mopped the floor and swept the sidewalk. He washed windows and bottles, and he had "a thousand bottles to dust." His salary was $3 a week.

His teacher, Miss Tillie Brown, summed up the character of her student in these words: "Harry was a determined and hard worker." At his graduation, as she kissed some of her students goodbye, among them Harry Truman, she said: "I hope yet to kiss a President of the United States."

Whether Bess Wallace hoped to kiss a President of the United States is not known. What *is* known is that the future wife of the President was his friend and companion from early childhood.

"From the fifth grade in school, until I graduated from

high school, we were in the same classes," Truman said. "If I succeeded in carrying her books to school, or back home for her, I had a big day."

The young sweethearts in Mark Twain's *Tom Sawyer*—a saga that takes place in another part of Missouri, Hannibal—have the same quality of simple affection as Bess Wallace and Harry Truman had during those idyllic years in Independence, Missouri.

# 2

The destiny of Harry S Truman took a very long time in revealing itself. There were too many influences at work. He could not make up his mind what he wanted to be. He seemed to drift from one activity to another—searching for an identity. This is not unusual, but in the case of Harry Truman, his destiny was clouded well into his mature years. Meanwhile he tried many things.

When he graduated from high school, he had hoped to go to college, but his father had lost his money. College was ruled out for Harry. He tried to get into West Point Military

Academy but was told that his weak eyesight barred him from that august institution. So the high-school graduate got a job.

"When I was eighteen," Truman recalls, "I was a timekeeper for a railroad contractor who was building a double track on the Santa Fe from a little town called Eaton Down, in the eastern end of Jackson County, to Sheffield. He had three gangs working and I used to have to go around and take the time, keep track of all the men who worked and all the teams on the job and then make out the checks."

Twice a day he pumped a handcar, going up and down the tracks inspecting the places where the gangs were working. This association with the tough railroad crews was an educational experience. He said he learned "all the cuss words in the English language—not by ear but by rote." When the job was finished, in June 1902, the foreman of the gang had this word of praise regarding the young timekeeper: "Harry's all right. He's all right from his navel out in every direction." The word "navel" seems a curious one for a tough foreman to use; perhaps history has cleaned up the language.

Harry got a job as a clerk with the National Bank of Commerce in Kansas City. It was dull work and the young clerk complained. "I don't have enough responsibility," he said. "I don't have anything to decide."

He quit that job in 1904 and became a bookkeeper at the Union National Bank. He lived in a boardinghouse where the brother of Dwight D. Eisenhower also happened to have a room. Arthur Eisenhower came from Abilene, Kansas, and was working as a bank clerk in Kansas City.

"Harry and I," he said, "had only a dollar a week left over for riotous living."

Harry made that dollar go far, and he added to it by taking a job Saturday afternoons, when the bank was closed. He worked as an usher in a vaudeville house.

And now an event occurred that was to be an important milestone in the life of this young man. It was the beginning of his political career. Yet, at the moment, politics was the last thing in his mind. Harry became a farmer. His father and mother had moved back to the family farm at Grandview, and young Harry was needed to help out.

He quit his bank job, and in the summer of 1906 the future President left lively Kansas City, left the bookkeeping business and took up residence on the old family homestead. He was twenty-two when he started a new career as a farmer.

For ten years Harry Truman was a farmer. He got up at 4:30 A.M. in the summer and 6:30 in winter. He plowed, sowed, reaped, milked cows, fed hogs, doctored horses, baled hay, "and did everything there was to do on a 600-acre farm."[1]

"My brother was a good farmer," Mary Jane Truman said.

[1] Man from Missouri, *and interview.*

"As my mother used to say, he could plow the straightest row of anybody she knew, and it's true. He was very particular about how he laid off the corn rows. And when he sowed the wheat in the fall, you very seldom saw a skipped place where he missed sowing any wheat. He was quite particular. He kept books on everything he did, and he raised fine hogs and some very good cattle. He was just a very good farmer and proud of it."[2]

This meticulousness, this attention to detail, was a characteristic that served him well throughout his life. And his years on the farm molded his character. All his life, he kept "farmer's hours." Later, when he was in power, he understood the problems of farmers as few Presidents before him had.

"A farmer," he said, "is one of those who really has time to think." And young Harry Truman did a lot of thinking. His affection for the family farm at Grandview never left him. When he moved back to Independence some eleven years later, and when he lived in Kansas City, even when at last he resided in Washington, D.C., he always returned to the farm from time to time.

"We always called it going back home. We always said we were going out home. We still say that."

The farm was Truman's home, actually and spiritually. And the independent spirit, the resourcefulness, the necessity to solve everyday practical problems, all of which is charac-

[2] *Interview.*

teristic of the farmer, became the mark of this man and remained with him for the rest of his life.

While Harry was running the farm at Grandview, his father became involved in politics through the Pendergast political machine, whose headquarters were in Kansas City.

A political machine was in those days, and perhaps is even now, often ruthless and corrupt. Certainly its leaders believed that the ends justify the means. The ends happened to be the winning of political power on every level—town, city, county, and state. The means to achieving political office included bribery, the stuffing of ballot boxes, and buying the good will of voters with favors and gifts. A politician found it difficult to attain his ends without the help of the political machine, and most officeholders belonged to the political machine and were, more or less, products of it, subject to the discipline of its leaders. Mike Pendergast was the powerful chief of the political machine that operated in Missouri.

With the help of the Pendergast machine, John Truman, Harry's father, was made an elections judge in the Grandview precinct. He supervised the voting at election time. Soon afterward he became a county delegate to the Missouri State Democratic Convention. Then one day John Truman became a road supervisor for Jackson County. He had a crew that looked after the bridges and the culverts, and he saw to it that the dirt farm roads were kept in good condition.

It is interesting to note that in time young Harry Truman followed this same pattern in his early political life. He did what his father did. For Harry, it was the beginning of a period of definite direction. He had been many things up to now. But soon he would find his identity in following in the footsteps of his father.

When John Truman died—and the death of a father is always a turning point in the life of a man—Harry Truman was thirty years old. He was now the head of the household. He continued to run the farm, but he also expanded his political activities. He took over his father's old job as road supervisor.

Immediately he advocated a more ambitious road program than the politicos in power were interested in supporting. Harry Truman put up a fight, and finally lost his job. In 1915, however, he was named postmaster of Grandview.

All this whetted his political appetite. He decided to learn how the Pendergast machine operated, and he began to travel into Kansas City to attend the Thursday-night meetings of the Kansas City Tenth Ward Democratic Club.

A friend, Tom Evans, reports: "During the meetings, when we talked about the elections and our political problems, we drank Irish beer and afterward drifted over to the nearest saloon for more. I first noticed Harry because he stood out from us roughnecks and he always left right after the meeting. We were all there for fun, but Harry seemed to be different."

Harry seemed to be different. No one could possibly

suspect that this modest, retiring, nearsighted young man was destined to hold the highest political office in the land.

All this while, he had not completely forgotten his school-days girl—Bess Wallace. She continued to live in a fine old house in Independence, twenty miles from Grandview, where Harry was running the farm.

Bess had been to a finishing school for girls in Kansas City. Now she was living with her widowed mother in the big house on North Delaware Street, in Independence. The Wallaces "had money," and they lived a comfortable, if not luxurious life.

After his father died, Harry began seeing Bess again. He was aware that his presence in the Wallace house was not overly welcomed by Bess's mother, Mrs. Madge Wallace. One of Harry's friends put the situation this way: "Harry was about the most unpromising prospect for a husband we had around here then. He had no money, no college education, and he lacked a future."[3]

One could understand the concern of Bess's mother regarding the man who was paying court to her daughter. How could Bess even consider marrying a common dirt farmer?

This is what Margaret Truman has to say about the courtship of her father and mother:

[3] *Quoted by Steinberg.*

"My father's nature is rarely so well expressed as in his singleminded devotion to my mother from early childhood. They are the same age and were friends and companions for twenty-five years before they were married. Their courtship, at least on my father's side of it, is legend. My father wooed her consistently—from a farm, where he had to commute twenty miles on Saturday nights by railroad train (in 1913 he bought a Stafford automobile to make commuting easier); he wooed her from a trench in France, while shot and shell were falling; from Kansas City, where he was working in a bank; and from wherever else he happened to be.

"I have no way of knowing how many times Dad proposed, and my mother would certainly say it was none of my business. Maybe it was only once. He's really a bashful man."

On the twenty-eighth of June, 1919, they were married in the same church where as a boy he had first seen her. Both were then thirty-five. It had taken a long time, but now at last they were man and wife.

In spite of his weak eyes, Harry had been to the wars in France, in charge of Battery D, a small outfit of field artillery whose members had been recruited largely from the Kansas City area. Eddie Jacobson was one of them and he was to play an important role in Truman's life. Among the top brass of the American Army in World War I was Brigadier General Douglas MacArthur. There was another man in that army who was to figure in Truman's future—

Colonel George Catlett Marshall. The paths of these military men were to enter the stream of Harry Truman's life in the decades to come.

But now the war had ended, and Harry Truman returned to Missouri and at last married his Bess. The couple moved into the bride's elegant house in Independence. It is not difficult to surmise the feelings of the groom, the former dirt farmer, as he moved through the damask-walled rooms of that house, over which his mother-in-law, the formidable Madge Wallace, presided.

# 3

Harry Truman, now a married man and no longer a farmer, set out to find some means of supporting himself and his wife.

One day, in Kansas City, he ran into Eddie Jacobson, who had been his buddy during the war. Eddie, too, was looking for something to do. He didn't want to go back to his former job as salesman on the road, selling men's shirts. The two of them decided to open up a men's furnishings store in Kansas City. Eddie knew how to buy the necessary merchandise, and Harry thought he could do "right well" behind the counter. Besides, he had been a bookkeeper and he could take charge of the books of the new business.

In a little while the two men signed a lease for a store across the street from the Hotel Muehlebach, which in later years was to become temporary Presidential headquarters.

"Truman and Jacobson" were open for business on November 29, 1919. Business boomed.

"We opened our store at 8 o'clock in the morning," Eddie Jacobson once told a reporter. "Those were the days when boys wore silk underwear and silk shirts. We sold silk shirts at sixteen dollars. Our business was all cash. No credit. Harry and I worked reverse shifts. Harry did the bookkeeping and I did the buying. We both did the selling."[1]

Sometimes Bess Truman came in from Independence and helped take inventory, and she went over the books for her husband and his baldheaded partner. The business flourished—but then in 1921, "after the Republicans took over the U. S. government under the Presidency of Warren G. Harding," says Truman, "Andrew Mellon was made Secretary of the Treasury. Farm prices dropped to an all-time low." Business at Truman and Jacobson's fell off drastically. Before too long, the business failed altogether and once again Harry Truman was casting about for some way of making a living.

[1] *Steinberg.*

23

One of the customers who used to come into the haberdashery was Jim Pendergast, of the powerful political organization that bore his name. Jim's father, Mike Pendergast, suggested that Harry Truman be supported for the candidacy of county judge, for not only had Harry's father known the politics of Jackson County, but Harry knew them almost as well.

"Mike Pendergast's suggestion appealed to me," says Truman. "I told him that I would like to run."

For a thirty-eight-year-old man without a job or even a prospect, the decision to run for county judge could not have been a very difficult one to make.

"The judges of those Missouri county courts," Truman explains, "are not judges in the ordinary sense. The court is an administrative body, not a judicial one. Among other things, the judge's duties were to levy taxes, look after the roads and the county buildings."[2]

Truman was nominated for the primaries with the help of Mike Pendergast, the boss of the Democratic political machine of the area. It was Truman's first venture into elective politics.

In an old Dodge jalopy, which he loaded down with two bags of cement to keep from being tossed through the windshield as he drove over the bumpy country roads, Harry S Truman embarked on his first campaign. He went

[2] Memoirs, *Vol. I.*

24

into every township and precinct in the county of his territory.

The candidate was well known for his bashfulness.

"The first speech I heard him make," reports a friend, "was the most painful thirty minutes I ever spent in my life."

And Truman corroborates the awful moment with this recollection: "My first political speech was made in 1922, in Sugar Creek, Missouri, and I was so scared when I went out on the platform that I couldn't say a word. So, I just got back off the platform." Not a very auspicious beginning for a man who would one day be President. Yet Truman, always plucky, did not give up.

"But," he continues, "from then on I learned how to make an appearance before an audience without becoming nervous and scared. And when the count was over, I won . . ."

In his *Memoirs* Truman, with characteristic modesty, attributes his victory to the fact that "I had relatives all over the county and through my wife I was related to many more."

At any rate, he was sworn into office and was now known as "Judge Truman." Though he did his job with typical thoroughness, he was "Judge" Truman for only a short while.

"In the next campaign," he says, "the Democratic Party split, and I was defeated for the first and only time in my political career."

But about this failure he is able to remark: "It was a good

thing, because I found out what a defeated candidate feels like."

It is obvious that Truman did not like what a defeated candidate felt like. He was determined not to experience failure again. When he ran for county judge again, he was elected. He now knew what he wanted to do in life. He was forty and was at last beginning to find his identity. He would be a politician. He wanted to have a college degree, so at this late age he enrolled in the Kansas City Law School. Harry Truman attended evening classes and studied hard, but after two years he dropped out. He did not get a college degree.

On February 17, 1924, the local Independence newspaper carried this item: "Judge and Mrs. Harry Truman announce the birth of a daughter at their home on Delaware Street Sunday morning."

Harry Truman was a doting father and spoiled his daughter Margaret whenever he got the chance. When she was eight, she yearned for a set of electric trains for Christmas.

"On Christmas morning," she reports, "when Daddy came to wake me, his face was shining like a new moon. [Margaret had been ill in bed with the flu.]

" 'Wait until you see,' he rhapsodized, wrapping me in a blanket. 'Wait until you see what you've got!'

"In my mind's eye," Margaret continues, "I saw the darling little electric train, running madly through minia-ture villages and over tiny bridges . . . I grinned and snuggled into his shoulder. He carried me down to the parlor.

" 'Well, there it is!' Daddy cried proudly and set me down in front of a shiny new baby-grand piano.

" 'Where?' I asked stupidly, looking around for the train.

" 'Right in front of you, Baby,' Daddy said.

"Out of disappointment and sheer weakness, I burst into tears and wouldn't touch the keys.

"Poor Daddy! It was certainly the most important and expensive present he had ever bought. He was earning a modest salary as presiding 'Judge' of the Jackson County Court. To him this piano was the most luxurious and wonderful present on earth."

Certainly Harry Truman must have felt badly at his young daughter's reaction. But in time she came to love his Christmas present, and Truman became his daughter's first piano teacher.

When Margaret grew older, she would drive around the county with her father while he inspected the roads, one of the jobs of his "judgeship." Mrs. Truman often accompanied them, and while father went about his inspections, mother and child picked flowers or bittersweet to take home. It was a happy, almost pastoral life.

The vast economic depression that had gripped the nation now began to strangle its economy. Truman was determined to expand the road-building program he had inaugurated in Jackson County. He believed that a public-works program would provide employment for the hundreds who had been thrown out of work. He also proposed the building of a new county courthouse in Kansas City. He was beginning to be known as an honest, productive politician, who could often be found in Brown's Drugstore on Independence Square, where he was available for advice and guidance.

In the years that followed, he fought for his program. He built new roads, new hospitals, and worried about the unemployment problem.

The year was 1933. Franklin Delano Roosevelt sat in the White House and wrestled with similar problems, and more.

The *St. Louis Globe-Democrat* noted that "Truman had been a district judge and a presiding judge for almost ten years." He was now in his late forties, and this appeared to be the sum and scope of his political career.

On his fiftieth birthday, a depressed Harry Truman sat in a hotel in Kansas City and ruminated about his life and career. The future appeared black. "I thought . . . that retirement in some minor county office was all that was in store for me."

# 4

No one has ever been able to find out just why the powerful Pendergast political machine chose Harry Truman to run for the United States Senate.

On May 14, Truman jotted down this note, which is a revelation not only of his state of mind but of his astringent character:

"It is 4 A.M. I am to make the most momentous announcement of my life. I have come to the place where all men strive to be at my age . . . In reading the lives of great men, I found that the first victory they won was *over themselves and their carnal urges. Self-discipline with all of them came first.*[1] I found that most of the really great ones never thought they were great. I could never admire a man whose only interest is himself . . . And now I am a candidate for the United States Senate. If the Almighty God decides that I go there I am going to pray as King Solomon did, for wisdom to do the job."

There was consternation in local political circles when it was learned that Truman had filed for the Senate race.

"I don't feel that Harry Truman has a chance," Pendergast has been quoted as saying. Then why had Truman been selected? But Pendergast had different statements for different people. "I want to put him in the Senate so I can get rid of him," he told someone else.

Whatever the reason, Harry Truman was the candidate for United States Senator, and he launched a vigorous campaign with this statement: "I know the farmer's problems, having been a dirt farmer for twelve years." Then he uttered magic words that were to assure him election, and he repeated them again, and again, wherever he spoke: "I am heart and soul for Franklin Delano Roosevelt."

Harry Truman was elected to the Senate of the United States. Suddenly life was startling. All their lives, the Trumans had lived in small towns or on farms, and now they were catapulted into the center of political life in America.

[1] *Italics are mine.*

"My mother," Margaret Truman reports, "who had lived in the same old house all her life, was now installed in a small furnished apartment—which appeared cramped and nondescript to her."

But Mrs. Truman and her daughter set out to visit the sights of Washington, D.C., like any other tourists. They stood in the long, slow-moving lines at the White House and, like hundreds of other tourists, were permitted to gaze briefly at the various State rooms. They certainly had no idea that a decade later they would occupy that very house.

As for Harry Truman, his painful provincialism caused him to be utterly uncomfortable in Washington. He was horrified by the rent he had to pay on the apartment. "I am undoubtedly the poorest Senator, financially, in Washington," he remarked. "I'll do my best and keep my feet on the ground. There isn't going to be any splurge—"

There certainly wasn't any splurge. Truman's sense of inadequacy had not left him, even though he had been elected to high office. He felt self-conscious about his lack of a college education. And in the fall he decided—he was then over fifty years old—that he would study law in evening school at Georgetown University. He had no idea how much work a Senator must do and how little time, if any, he would have for formal studies at night school.

He made a touching statement on his arrival in Washington which reveals his utter humility at the prospect before him. He considered himself "only a humble member of the next Senate, green as grass and ignorant as a fool about practically everything worth knowing."[2]

While the modesty of the statement is attractive, it also reveals the sense of insignificance which the new Senator felt at the time. After a lifetime of trying one thing after another, and failing in most of them, Harry Truman, in his middle age, was about to find himself.

"It was a great day for me in January 3, 1935, when I entered the chamber of the United States Senate to take my seat for the first time. Although I was nearly fifty-one years old at the time, I was as timid as a country boy arriving on the campus of a great university for his first year."[3]

As a freshman Senator, Truman worked like a Trojan. He got to his office at seven o'clock in the morning and returned home for dinner twelve hours later. During those early days he rarely opened his mouth on the floor of the Senate. He dealt with issues he knew best: farm problems and legislation having to do with highways. He made it his business to learn all the details of any bill that came up for vote.

He voted for the Wagner Labor Relations Act of 1935, noting that "a law to give the working people equality at the bargaining table was a necessity."

He voted for the Social Security Act of 1935—"although it lacked health insurance for hospital and doctors' bills. I tried

[2] *Daniels.*
[3] Memoirs.

32

to remedy this lack when I became President." He supported all the measures of Roosevelt's New Deal—a program that revolutionized the American economy and changed and revitalized the role of government in the United States.

As the months passed, it is almost possible to see Harry Truman's character firming up, changing. The cloud that his antagonists had spread over him—that he was a politician made by the Pendergast machine, that he was Pendergast's "office boy" in the Senate—began to hang heavy over the new Senator's head. He resolved to do something about it.

"I don't follow his [Pendergast's] advice on legislation," he is quoted as saying. "I vote the way I believe Missourians as a whole would want me to vote."

The man from Independence was beginning to feel the necessity for his own independence.

"I'm tired of being pushed around," he said, "tired of having the President treat me like an office boy." He telephoned F.D.R. at the White House and said just that to the President. It was Harry Truman's personal declaration of independence. He had sat silently in the United States Senate for almost a year and a half. Now he knew his way about and he began to reveal a newfound power.

He became a friend of the great liberal judge of the Supreme Court, Louis D. Brandeis.

Truman had never been an intellectual, but he was drawn to the venerable Brandeis and to the ideas that were discussed in his apartment. Here was an atmosphere Truman had never before encountered. Through Brandeis he met men of ideas and ideals. Politics to them was not only a process of vote getting and political machines; it was a dedication, the highest calling to which man could attain.

Old Judge Brandeis, the liberal judge, was attracted to the unassuming, modest junior Senator from Missouri. And in Brandeis's circle Truman found a new world. It was to influence him the rest of his life.

The liberal cloak that Truman now wore was revealed in one of the most astounding speeches he ever made—an attack on concentrated wealth and on the "bankers and lawyers who not only slavishly served this great wealth but who guarded it zealously from the common people."

Truman had been investigating the prostrated railroads. "I ransacked the Library of Congress for every book on the subject of railroad management and history," he says. "I saw in my assignment . . . a genuine opportunity to get to the bottom of the dishonest practices which had wrecked some of our greatest carrier systems, and I dedicated myself to pushing the inquiry until the whole truth was revealed."

Truman sounded his political philosophy with a slashing attack on "big business."

"The railroad investigations," he said, "had shown that such great law firms as Davis, Polk, Wardwell, Gardner and Reed of New York . . . had resorted to tricks that would make an ambulance chaser in a coroner's court blush with shame." He went on to attack the powerful charitable

34

organization known as the Rockefeller Foundation, saying that it was "founded on the dead miners of the Colorado Fuel and Iron Company [which the Rockefellers owned]."

The shape and color of his political thinking became utterly clear in this remarkable speech, and he has never veered from it.

Truman was a hard and conscientious worker in the Senate. Every evening he rode home from his office on the local city bus, carrying his papers and books with him.

"I remember sitting on the bus one afternoon with my nose in my homework," Margaret Truman reports. "Suddenly I was hit on the head with a folded newspaper which had been thrown at me. I looked around furiously . . . There sat Dad, laughing his head off."

Truman's first term in the Senate was drawing to a close and he had to decide whether he would run for a second term. The President, Franklin Roosevelt, sent a message to Harry Truman offering him an appointment on the Interstate Commerce Commission. Truman interpreted the offer as a way of forestalling Truman's running for the Senate for a second term. It has been said, too, that in this message F.D.R. told Truman that he didn't believe Truman had a chance to be renominated in Missouri. This certainly must have gotten Truman's dander up. He replied to F.D.R.'s message: "I sent him word, that I would run if I only got one vote—MINE."

F.D.R. was in fact backing Truman's opponent. The prospects for reelection didn't look good.

When Truman got back to Missouri, his friends all advised him not to run. The Pendergast machine had been investigated and its operations exposed.

"I realized that attempts would be made to link my name with the misdeeds and misfortunes of Pendergast and to make it appear that I was the product of a corrupt political machine."

But Truman was not too much disturbed by this. He knew he had an unblemished record which he could cite, but he was aware of the damage false propaganda could cause. Then, too, Truman had no political organization, nor did he have any money with which to wage a campaign.

Nevertheless, he ran in the primaries against the popular and powerful governor of Missouri, Lloyd Stark, who also wanted to be United States Senator.

Truman opened his campaign at a time when the Nazis were overrunning Europe. Paris had just surrendered. America was disturbed and worried about the world situation. Politics at home were regarded as secondary.

On June 15, on the courthouse steps at Sedalia, Missouri, Harry S Truman opened his battle for a seat in the Senate. He was introduced by his friend Lewis Schwellenback, who said, "I need not tell you that Harry Truman is not an orator. He can demonstrate that for himself." Another friend said that "Harry was such a bad speaker it was pitiful."

With his eighty-eight-year-old mother sitting on the platform, Truman began his speech.

"I always make it my business to speak plainly and directly to the people without indulging in high-powered oratory. The truth, I feel, is what voters need more than anything else, and when they have that, they can vote intelligently."

The people seemed to agree with him. They listened intently in Sedalia, Missouri, as he talked about civil rights:

"I believe in the brotherhood of man, not merely the brotherhood of white men but the brotherhood of all men before law . . . In the years past, lynching and mob violence, lack of schools, and countless other unfair conditions hastened the progress of the Negro from the country to the city . . . They have been forced to live in segregated slums, neglected by the authorities."

The people liked Harry Truman's plain speaking. They believed in his sincerity. They liked his scrappiness.

Truman carried out a hard-hitting campaign, touring seventy-five counties, making ten talks a day, shaking hands with as many people as he could, sleeping in the car en route to the next stop.

In the last two weeks of the campaign, however, money ran out. There was only $200 in the treasury. Truman borrowed $3,000 on his life-insurance policy, and his friend Harry Vaughn addressed 13,000 letters with this message: "If you want to see Harry Truman returned to the Senate, send

$1 immediately." In two days, and from every part of the state, $1,800 had come in.

Election day, August 6, showed that Stark was far in the lead almost from the beginning. By ten o'clock that night, Truman was ready to concede: "I went to bed defeated," he said.

But at eleven o'clock in the morning it was apparent to everyone that Harry S Truman had won the election. F.D.R. wrote, congratulating him on his victory. There was no doubt about it: there was something about the style of the peppery Mr. Truman which the voters liked.

Now Truman, the Democratic nominee, had to fight the Republican nominee for the United States Senate, Marselle Davis. He defeated Davis and now was U. S. Senator from Missouri in his own right. He had won without the Pendergast machine.

When he entered the Senate chamber following his exhausting campaign, he was given a standing ovation by his colleagues. This simple, unadorned man had proved himself a fighter and a winner. He was fifty-six years old. It had been a long journey with many twists and turns, but the future now lay clearly before him.

# 5

In his second term as Senator from Missouri, Truman became a national figure. He became someone to reckon with. The United States was not yet at war, but it had become the great arsenal of democracy. Not only were we feverishly building up our own defenses as Hitler's armies scored success after success in Europe, but we were sending Britain and Russia supplies: ammunition, tanks, planes. Our defense industries became the single most important factor in the country's economy.

Truman, you will remember, had always kept books. As a

haberdasher and as a farmer he knew what came in, what was the cost, and how much went out. He was thorough, meticulous; an excellent bookkeeper. Now these qualities were to make his name.

Billions of dollars of American tax money were being appropriated to pay for the cost of expanding airplane plants and for the construction of new ones.

"I was concerned about charges that the huge contracts and the immense purchases that resulted from these appropriations were being handled through favoritism. I saw cliques in labor and in capital each greedy for gain; the big fellows, in the name of government, were putting thousands of small concerns out of business."

Senator Truman was concerned. He got into his car and started out from Washington to make an investigation on his own. He drove 30,000 miles through Maryland down to Florida, across to Texas, north through Oklahoma and Nebraska, and back through Wisconsin and Michigan.

"I visited war camps, defense plants, and other establishments and projects . . . and did not let any of them know who I was," Truman says. "The trip was an eye-opener, and I came back to Washington convinced that something needed to be done fast."

The result was the formation of a Senate Investigating Committee, called the "Special Committee to Investigate the National Defense Program." Its chairman was Harry S Truman, and before long the press and the people across the nation began calling it the "Truman Committee."

The fairness and vigor that Truman brought to his task soon made him a national figure, much admired. This scrappy little man became synonymous with fearlessness. One day, in the midst of a coal strike that threatened the defense effort, he sent a telegram to a group of Southern coal operators. "Your faction," Truman said bluntly, "is holding up settlement. We know your mines are owned by northern capitalists and bankers. If you don't end this deadlock within twenty-four hours, we are going to send for these capitalists and bankers. We intend to put them on the witness stand and find out from them, as principals, whether the national safety or the wage dispute comes first."

This was rough, tough talk. There was no shilly-shallying, and Truman's telegram brought immediate results. The deadlock was ended that very night and a settlement agreed upon.

It was obvious to all that Truman enjoyed his work as chairman of the committee. His soul seemed to expand. He had found his stride at last. His prestige and power increased. He was no longer just another obscure junior Senator with no visible political future. Even Franklin Roosevelt, who up to now had been rather cool to this blunt-speaking Midwesterner, began to take notice of him and of his work on the committee. The committee had recommended the creation of a War Production Board under the direction of a single chairman.

"By the time of my first report to the Senate," Truman records, "the President had already announced his intention

41

to create such an agency. Thus President Roosevelt received public credit for the War Production Board because of his advance knowledge of the committee's report. That was all right with me. I wanted action more than credit."

One gloomy Sunday in December, Harry Truman, dog-tired, was spending the day in a small hotel in Columbia, Missouri. He had decided he needed rest and sleep after his weeks and months of rugged investigations.

In Washington, in the small apartment where they lived, Margaret Truman was listening to the Sunday broadcast of the Philharmonic Symphony.

"They keep breaking into the symphony," Margaret complained to her mother in the next room. "They keep saying something about the Japanese attacking Pearl Harbor—wherever that is."

"Pearl Harbor is in Hawaii!" Bess Truman cried.

"It was then borne in on me [as it was for millions of other Americans]," Margaret reports, "that Japanese planes had attacked the United States.

"My mother ran to the telephone and put in a call to the Tennant Hotel in Columbia, Missouri. She woke my father out of a sound sleep . . . Daddy said later that he was frantic. He knew that he had to be back in Washington . . . but he was far from established airlines. He leapt into his clothes and walked across the fields to a little private airport and stated his predicament. The owner of the airport borrowed a private plane and flew him to St. Louis, where he managed to get on a plane for Washington."

He was in the House chamber when President Roosevelt, the following morning, declared war.

The nation was at war, and the real work of the Truman Committee began. A number of fatalities had occurred among pilots flying the B-26 Martin bomber. Truman investigated and found that the wingspread of the Martin bomber was too short.

Glenn Martin, testifying at one of the hearings, said that the blueprints of this plane were already on the board and that he would have to go through with the project.

"I told Martin," Truman reports, "that if the lives of American boys depended upon the planes . . . the committee would see to it that no defective ships were purchased."

"Well," Martin replied, "if that's the way you feel about it, we'll change it."

A similar situation occurred with defective engines produced at the Wright Aeronautical Corporation. These engines were causing the death of student pilots. The committee condemned some four hundred of these engines, but officials of both the company and the Army said nothing was wrong with the engines.

Truman's subcommittee then went out to the plant and held hearings.

Before it had finished, it had heard scores of witnesses who testified that defective parts and defective engines had passed inspection at the plant and had been turned over to the Army. The Army conducted an investigation on its own and finally agreed with the facts turned up by the subcommittee. This dangerous and dishonest practice was then brought to an end.

The committee was responsible for saving billions of dollars of taxpayers' money. What is more, the committee had saved lives.

Out to make a swift dollar, a subsidiary of the United States Steel Corporation which manufactured steel plate for the Navy cheated on the tensile strength of the steel plate. The physical tests made on this plate were "faked and falsified."

The company men in charge of the operation with the testing machines testified that about five percent or more of the tests were deliberately faked and the steel plate falsely reported to be in accordance with specifications. To do this they [the company men] instructed the testers under them to cheat.

The outraged committee, which had become the conscience of the nation, said that the only excuse they would accept was an "early and complete correction."

There were other areas in which the committee was effective; one was the stockpiling of raw material.

"One day, Dad brought home a shoe heel made of synthetic rubber," Margaret Truman reported. "He said it was a secret, but soon we would have a lot of things made out of synthetic rubber." And Margaret notes in her diary, skeptically: "I wonder."

But Truman was not satisfied to remain on the sidelines, in spite of the valuable work he was doing. He, a man in his middle fifties, wanted to get into the actual fighting. He went to see his friend General George C. Marshall, who was Chief of Staff, and offered his services.

"Senator Truman," Marshall said, "you've got a big job to do right up there at the Capitol with your Investigating Committee. Besides, Senator, this is a young man's war. We don't need any old stiffs like you."

"I am younger than you, General Marshall."

"Yes, but I'm a general and you'd only be a colonel. You stay right where you are."[1]

Harry Truman stayed where he was. But destiny was working behind the scenes.

"Early in 1944 some of my friends began to suggest that I become a candidate for Vice-President," writes Truman. "I had never entertained such an idea, and whenever the suggestion was made I brushed it aside."

His friend Max Lowenthal, who had first introduced Truman to Supreme Court Justice Brandeis, remembers a talk he had with the chairman of the Investigating Committee.

"Truman said he had talked it [the Vice-Presidency] over

[1] *Quoted in Walter Hehmeyer,* Harry Truman: President.

45

with the Mrs. and had decided not to be a candidate. 'I've got a daughter and the limelight is no place for children.' "[2]

Truman told Lowenthal, moreover, that he was too poor to think about running.

What is most significant about his friends urging Truman to run for the Vice-Presidency is that the modest, unknown Senator had become well known across the nation as the vigorous chairman of an investigating committee which was rooting out graft and cheating, and saving the American people billions of dollars.

On March 8, 1943, the unadorned visage of Harry S Truman, former dirt farmer, county road supervisor, and haberdasher, appeared on the cover of *Time* magazine. He was now an outstanding Senator. People invited him to speak. He had never been an orator, yet he accepted lecture engagements. And although other Senators got several thousand dollars a year on the lecture circuit, Harry Truman always refused to accept a fee.

The work of his committee continued to receive praise, and when a poll of Washington newspaper correspondents indicated that after President Roosevelt he was the man who had done most for the war effort, his position as a national figure appeared to be secure. He was now a man to be reckoned with for one of the highest offices of the land. Truman was modest about it all. "I haven't changed," he said. "I am the same person I was five or ten years ago."

[2] Souvenir.

But was he? He *had* changed. He was sure of himself. He had found himself.

The Vice-President was Henry Wallace, F.D.R.'s personal choice. But he was losing favor not only with Roosevelt, but with Democratic political bosses such as Ed Flynn, Frank Kelly, and Edwin Pauley, the National Committee Treasurer. They were all opposed to Wallace's running for Vice-President again. Even before the 1944 Democratic Convention, it had been agreed that F.D.R. must run for a fourth term. What remained open was the choice of a running mate.

The ways of political life are not as mysterious as they appear. It was Robert Hannegan who first proposed to Roosevelt that he accept Truman as the Vice-Presidential candidate in the 1944 election.

Hannegan, in 1942, had been appointed to the post of Collector of Internal Revenue at St. Louis. It was Harry Truman who had been instrumental in securing Hannegan's appointment.

Now, in January 1944, Hannegan had risen so high in the ranks of the Democratic Party that he assumed the chairmanship of the National Committee of the party. Soon after, he and the other political bosses went to the White House to talk over the impending National Convention with the President. Since it had been agreed that Roosevelt must run for a fourth term, the discussion centered on the choice of a Vice-Presidential candidate. Hannegan suggested Truman, his friend and benefactor. The other politicos also felt that Truman would make a first-rate candidate. Through his work in the Investigating Committee he had become well-known, popular, and respected all over the country. Roosevelt listened, but it is reported he made no comment.

There was a great deal of jockeying about the Vice-Presidential candidate from that first meeting with Roosevelt in January until the very day of the convention in July. Various names were suggested to Roosevelt, including James Byrnes, who was the "assistant President."

Bob Hannegan never stopped working on behalf of the candidacy of Harry Truman. When at last the time came for Hannegan to reveal his plans to Truman, the potential candidate appeared reluctant. He felt the President would be against him as a candidate since Truman's committee had often attacked Roosevelt's war agencies. Then too, he felt, the Republicans would find plenty of ammunition to attack him with since he had never repudiated his association with the Pendergast machine and had no intention of doing so now.

It must have been a curious period for Harry Truman as he looked back over his life, his failure in business, his lack of a college education, the humbleness of his background, to find himself, in his late fifties, being considered for candidate for Vice-President of the United States.

The President, well-born, a Hudson River aristocrat, a Groton and Harvard graduate, well-traveled and sophisticated, would certainly hesitate to have as his running mate this raw, plain-speaking man from the farmlands of Missouri.

As the convention neared, Hannegan was increasingly aware that F.D.R. was leaning toward James Byrnes as his choice. Hannegan went to work. He slyly attempted to undermine Byrnes in the President's eyes, meanwhile telling Byrnes that "he was the right man for the Vice-President and that Roosevelt thought so too. Byrnes was flattered. Biding his time in this manner, he [Hannegan] hoped to reduce Byrnes' natural aggressiveness and finally render him harmless."[3]

All the while, however, Hannegan was working on behalf of Truman. Thus it has been with politicians from the days of Pericles and Caesar.

Into this classic pattern, however, another element was to be introduced: the President was soon to die.

"Signs of failing health in the President were unmistakable," Ed Flynn said. "His usual pep and keen interest in things were missing." The men around Roosevelt were convinced that he would not live through another term. The choice of his successor, therefore, was of utmost importance.

Churchill, too, was to notice the President's waning health at the conference of the Big Three—Roosevelt, Stalin, and Churchill—at Yalta.

". . . I noticed that the President was ailing. His captivat-

[3] *Steinberg.*

49

ing smile, his gay and charming manner, had not deserted him, but his face had a transparency, an air of purification, and often there was a far-away look in his eyes. When I took my leave of him . . . I must confess that I had an indefinable sense of fear that his health and his strength were on the ebb."[4]

And so the drama was set. The President was ill. He might die. The bosses wanted *their* man in the Chief Executive's seat. They backed their man for the position of Vice-President, knowing that it would be but for a little while. The "little man," Harry Truman, might soon become "the big man," if only he could be elected Vice-President.

The 1944 National Democratic Convention opened in July, in Chicago.

In her diary Margaret Truman records the following items:

JULY 17, 1944

We are on our way to Chicago. Hope it will be fun but probably not very exciting.

JULY 18, 1944

Arrived in Chicago. Staying in suite at the Morrison. There is talk of Daddy for Vice-President. Just a rumour I'm sure.

JULY 19, 1944

Ye gods! The Missouri delegation has decided to nominate Dad for V-P. Vice-President Wallace is very strong so doubt if we win . . .

[4] *Churchill,* Triumph and Tragedy, p. 477.

JULY 20, 1944

Pres. Roosevelt was nominated for a fourth term . . . went shopping at Marshall Fields and got lost!

A BIG JULY 21, 1944 DAY

All I can write after such a day is *whew!!* Daddy has been nominated for Vice-President to run with President Roosevelt . . . The Convention went wild.

Of her father in that year of destiny, 1944, Margaret writes:

"His star rose with the sudden brilliance of a comet. If he had reservations about his appointments with destiny, they were concerned to a degree with me. He is a thoughtful man and did not wish to deprive me of the opportunity of making a life on my own terms. For several days [at the 1944 convention] he flouted every suggestion that he should be nominated . . . the choice of my father was a complete upset. Dad delivered . . . the shortest nomination acceptance speech in the history of the United States—ninety-two words."

Speaking of her mother and father, Margaret says: "Police and Secret Service men surrounded the three of us. My mother said almost piteously to my father, 'Are we going to have to go through this the rest of our lives?'

"She appeared to blame her poor husband for the sudden and unusual position in which she, the quiet woman from North Delaware Street, Independence, Missouri, had found herself.

"Dad was too tired to say anything," Margaret records, "and he had a nomination he didn't want."

After the convention, the Trumans returned to their house in Independence and held an open reception in their back yard. Margaret notes in her diary:

"Shook hands with our 3,000 fellow townspeople and out-of-towners. All of us dog-tired."

And now Harry Truman was the candidate for the Vice-Presidency of the United States. Destiny was closing in. One incident has been recorded which reveals how tenuous a thing fate can be.

When Hannegan was first trying to get Roosevelt to consider his friend Harry Truman for the Vice-Presidency, one problem bothered Hannegan. At their meeting in the White House, F.D.R. admitted to Hannegan that Truman had done a fine job as chairman of the Investigating Committee, but, Roosevelt added, he didn't know Truman very well personally. He wanted to know how old Truman was. Wasn't he about sixty? Roosevelt sent for a *Congressional Directory* to find out Truman's exact age.

Hannegan realized that this was a crisis. If F.D.R. learned that Truman *was* sixty, it would definitely strike him out as a candidate. The political bosses meeting with F.D.R. at the time engaged him in lively conversation immediately, thus distracting him, and he eventually forgot to ask further about Truman's age. He said to Hannegan: "Bob, I think you and everyone else here want Truman." At that, the bosses left the session, before F.D.R. remembered that he had sent for the *Congressional Directory*.

It was a narrow squeak. But fate was working for Truman.

Truman had been born in Lamar, Missouri, the home of the bandit and outlaw Jesse James. It was on the courthouse steps of Lamar that Truman got the news officially from Senator Tom Connally that he had been selected as the Democratic nominee for Vice-President.

The pride that his eighty-six-year-old mother must have felt, remembering the day her son was born, her son who had now been chosen to run for Vice-President, has not been recorded. But it must have been keen.

Before the campaign began, the family had to move back to Washington. Besides, daughter Margaret was due to return to school. Harry Vaughn, Truman's old friend, lent the Trumans the two cars that were to carry their belongings to their center of operations. Some of the stuff was loaded on top of the cars. Then the two men got into the cars and drove off, looking for all the world like "pioneers on a trek."[5]

Bess and Margaret Truman went by train. "The wartime trains were so crowded there was hardly room to move. We stood in line for hours trying to get into the diner and finally gave up and went back and ate candy bars for dinner."

[5] *Souvenir.*

53

Apparently there was no protocol for the family of a Vice-Presidential candidate.

When they reached the apartment, Bess Truman and Margaret set about giving their living quarters a thorough cleaning while Harry Truman set out across the country for a month-long speaking tour.

"Roosevelt told me that he was so busy in the war effort," Truman says, "that I would have to do the campaigning for both of us." They were meeting alone at the White House.

They had lunch at a small table under a magnolia tree that had been planted on the White House grounds by Andrew Jackson, who, as everyone knew, was Truman's favorite President. It was a very hot day and the two most important political figures on the American scene sat in their shirt sleeves as they ate sardines on toast. Roosevelt, whose health was obviously failing, said that Truman would make the campaign on a train, not by airplane—"because one of us has to stay alive." The climax of Harry Truman's life was fast approaching.

"The campaign of 1944 was the easiest in which I had ever participated. The Republican candidates [Thomas E. Dewey of New York and Earl Warren, who was Vice-Presidential candidate on the Republican ticket] never had a chance." Truman traveled around the country plugging the New Deal theme to "put human welfare first and profits second."

It was difficult for the Republicans to launch an attack on Roosevelt. He had led the nation out of the worst depression in history and he was leading America to a victorious conclusion of the European and Pacific wars. The Republicans tried to make an issue of Roosevelt's health. They insinuated that he was gravely ill.

Truman's venerable mother had listened to the Republican convention on the radio. She sat on her rocking chair in the parlor of her Grandview home and said: "I tried not to hate them [the Republicans]. They kept predicting that Roosevelt will die in office if he's elected. I hope Roosevelt fools them. I'm not a giggly woman, but I can't help smiling when people cheer at the mention of Harry's name."

The Republicans blundered again when they said F.D.R. had sent a destroyer to the Aleutian Islands to bring back his dog, Fala.

F.D.R. retorted with scathing scorn: "The Republican leaders have not been content to make personal attacks upon me—or my wife—or my sons—they now include my little dog, Fala."

The Republicans were in difficulty. They turned their attack on the Democratic candidate for Vice-President. Herbert Brownell, Jr., who was chairman of the Republican National Committee, said the Republican campaign would expose "the unfitness of the Democratic candidate for Vice-President, Senator Truman."

One magazine said: "The competence of Mr. Roosevelt's current running mate is the nearest thing the country has to a burning issue."

Truman campaigned hard, but on the eve of the election

Roosevelt was worried. At Hyde Park on the Hudson, F.D.R. sat in the dining room listening to the early returns. Friends reported that he was dejected, certain that "that so-and-so in Albany [Dewey]," whom he had vowed to beat if it was the last thing he did, was winning the election. Margaret Truman presents what she calls a "girl's-eye view" of the final days of the election, taken from her diary.

NOV. 1, 1944

I am on the special car [her father's campaign train]. It has a private dining room and kitchen, lounge and shower bath and 5 compartments. It's beautiful. We stopped at Parkersburg for a parade and meeting tonight. Grand meeting!

NOV. 2, 1944

What a day! The crowds were terrific [in Pittsburgh]. Orson Welles had dinner with us and then spoke on the same plat-form as Dad. Daddy made about 10 speeches today.

NOV. 3, 1944

We're in the Penthouse in the Muehlebach Hotel, in Kansas City [which Truman used as his local headquarters].

NOV. 7, 1944

I had a voice lesson and spent half the day listening to Galli-Curci records and singing. I'm going on the radio . . . in the morning if we win.

I stayed up all night and WE'VE WON!

All through that tense election night, Truman had seen his friends growing more and more depressed as the returns came in, indicating a Republican victory. When the early Missouri returns started coming in, pointing to a definite Republican trend, Truman said: "I think that calls for a concert." And he sat down at the piano and began playing Paderewski's *Minuet*.

He waited all through the night with his friends. It was almost four o'clock in the morning when Dewey finally conceded defeat. The Democratic victory was overwhelming: 432 electoral votes, to 99 for the Republicans.

Harry S Truman was now Vice-President of the United States. He had come a long way from Lamar, Missouri, a long way from the farm in Grandview, from the home on North Delaware in Independence, Missouri. And yet, in spirit, he had never left them.

Now he held the second highest political position in the United States. He was to be Vice-President for only eighty days.

# 6

Only two Presidents in the history of the United States had ever been inaugurated while the country was at war. One was James Madison; the other, Abraham Lincoln. Now Franklin Delano Roosevelt, inaugurated for a fourth term, was to become the third.

"On Jan. 20, 1945, a snowy Saturday, I stood on the south portico of the White House beside President Roosevelt," writes Truman. "A crowd of several thousand had gathered on the White House lawn to witness the ceremony."

As everyone knows, the swearing-in ceremonies usually

take place on the steps of the Capitol and not at the White House, so it appears that from the very beginning, the Vice-Presidential life of Harry Truman took on a special character. The retiring Vice-President, Henry Wallace, administered the oath to Truman. "In a matter of minutes," Truman remarks, "I was the new Vice-President of the United States. I stepped back, and President Roosevelt took his place . . . to receive the oath of office for his fourth term."

"He [Roosevelt] wore a dark suit and no overcoat," writes Margaret, who was present, ". . . he looked tired and made several impatient gestures to James [his son] and the people around him . . . When he stood up . . . he stood there in the freezing wind, bareheaded and without a coat.

"I suddenly felt horribly depressed. All the world seemed to me to have turned to gray ice . . ."

Why would a young girl whose father had just become Vice-President of the United States feel suddenly dejected? There must have been some foreboding in the air to bring on this melancholy. Others have noted it, too. It was more than the weather. It was painfully obvious that the man who had just been sworn in as President of the United States was tired, exhausted, and had little zest for life, and little energy. He was a depleted man.

After the ceremonies there was an official luncheon, but "the newly-sworn President was not present."

"I can't get my husband to eat," Mrs. Roosevelt said in a worried tone of voice. "He just won't eat."

After the luncheon, Harry Truman slipped out of the White House, hitched a ride to Capitol Hill, and telephoned his mother, who had listened to the ceremonies over the radio in her parlor in Grandview, Missouri.

"Did you listen to the radio?" her son asked her.

"Yes," his old mother said. "I heard it all. Now, you behave yourself up there, Harry. You behave yourself." The new sixty-year-old Vice-President promised his mother that he would behave.

On January 20, 1945, the day Truman became Vice-President, it was apparent that German resistance in Europe was crumbling before the Allied onslaught. The last great German attack in the Ardennes—countered in the Battle of the Bulge—had collapsed. The Germans were being pushed back across their own devastated country. German cities had been pulverized by Allied bombings.

Victory in the European Theater appeared imminent, but the situation in the Pacific was not good. There victory seemed a long way off. The Japanese fought with a ferocity unknown in the annals of war. Millions of American and British soldiers, it was evident, would perish before Tokyo could be taken.

Two days after Truman took the oath of office as Vice-President, Roosevelt left Washington for a conference with Churchill and Stalin at Yalta on the Black Sea.

Four days later, Tom Pendergast, Truman's friend and

mentor and the head of the Pendergast political machine in Missouri, died, a discredited and dishonored man. It would have been wise politics for Truman to ignore the death of his old friend who had been in jail for "fraud and corruption." But this was not in the Truman code of ethics. Truman flew to Kansas City for Pendergast's funeral.

"I'm sorry as I can be," Truman said about Pendergast's death. "He was always my friend and I have always been his." Truman was violently attacked for attending the funeral, but he ignored his critics. He could not forget that it was Pendergast who had started him on his political career.

As Vice-President, Truman had little to do except preside over the Senate and attend social functions. The Vice-President is not an officer of the executive branch of the government and he does not sit in on Cabinet meetings, except at the invitation of the President.

There were few Cabinet meetings, since Roosevelt was either out of the country or at Warm Springs, Georgia, for his health. Truman was an "outsider," a fifth wheel, and he felt useless and superfluous.

On the afternoon of April 12 he was presiding over the Senate, bored and restless. He decided to write a letter home to his mother and sister:

"Dear Mama and Mary," he wrote, "I am trying to write you a letter from the desk of the President of the Senate while a windy Senator is making a speech on a subject with which he is in no way familiar."

Then he goes on to say: "Turn on your radio tomorrow

night at 9:30 your time, and you'll hear Harry make a Jefferson Day address to the nation . . . It will be followed by the President, whom I'll introduce."[1]

The Senate that day recessed at ten minutes after five. Truman was almost immediately summoned to the White House. At 5:25, at the White House, he learned that Franklin Delano Roosevelt was dead. He had died in Warm Springs. Less than two hours later, at 7:09, Harry S Truman was President of the United States.

"Dad's face was grief-stricken and worried," his daughter Margaret remembers. "I had a rush of compassion for him. I prayed my wordless prayers: Give him the strength. Let everything be all right. Let him be equal to it. Let him live through it."

Truman went to his new office at the White House on Friday the thirteenth. If he was superstitious, and the date foreboding to him, he never showed it. It was a tough day for Truman. Many members of Roosevelt's loyal staff found it difficult to remember that Truman was now President. Two days later, at Roosevelt's funeral, not a single member of the Cabinet got to his feet, as is customary, when the President walked into the room. Apparently they had forgotten that Truman was the new Chief Executive.

"I knew," Truman remarked, "that I was not the first whose destiny it was to be thrust suddenly into the shoes of history's great leaders. But I would take each decision in

[1] *Steinberg.*

turn. Mr. Roosevelt's Cabinet would remain in office. Mr. Roosevelt's policies—foreign and domestic—would be continued.

"But I made it clear that I was President in my own right, and that I would assume full responsibility for such decisions as had to be made."

Truman had a decision to make almost immediately. A conference had been planned for April 25 at San Francisco. It was here that the United Nations was to be organized. The Secretary of State, Edward Stettinius, wanted to know if the conference would proceed as planned.

"I did not hesitate a second," Truman remembers. "The conference would be held. It was the first decision I had made as President."

Then suddenly some awe-inspiring knowledge came to the new President. It was something which up to that moment he had been unaware of. He, the Vice-President, successor to the highest office in the nation, had been kept in the dark about the development of the atomic bomb, which was even then being perfected by our scientists. Truman received the information after his first Cabinet meeting.

"After the Cabinet left," Truman says, "the Secretary of War Stimson stayed behind. He told me something even I had never known. Something about the awful power that might soon be mine to decide about."

Truman was faced with the enormity of the job into which destiny had led him. He had to decide about the future conduct of the war, about the peace which would follow, about the shape of the world which would evolve. The lives of future generations of Americans depended upon the wisdom of his decisions.

"After the Cabinet meeting, I left. I had a lot to think about. I was tired. So I left the taxpayers' house [the White House] to go home [to his apartment] and face the music. I knew Mrs. Truman and Margaret would be unhappy. We would none of us live our own lives again.

"I had not had anything to eat since noon. Our next-door neighbors gave us some turkey left over from dinner. Then I went to bed and did not worry any more that day."

But there would be plenty to worry about in the days to come.

# Part Two

Part Two

# 7

"Dear Mama and Mary," Truman wrote a few days after he had become President, ". . . this afternoon we moved to this house [Blair House], diagonally across the street from the White House, until the Roosevelts have had time to move out of the White House. We tried staying at the apartment, but it wouldn't work. I can't move without at least ten Secret Service men and twenty policemen. People who lived in our apartment couldn't get in and out without a pass. So—we moved with our suitcases. Our furniture is still there and will be for some time . . . But I've paid the rent for this month. Soon as we get settled in the White House, you'll both be here to visit us. Lots of love from your very much worried son and bro.

Harry"

Truman had much to be worried about. Among other things, he was facing his first meeting with Stalin and Churchill. He was inexperienced in foreign affairs and now he would soon be dealing with these giants.

He had addressed a joint session of Congress the same afternoon he wrote his mother. He was so affected by the sight of the Senators, the Representatives, the justices of the Supreme Court, the Cabinet, and the diplomatic corps—to say nothing of seeing his wife and daughter in the gallery— all gathered to hear his first official address, that he started to speak as soon as he got to the rostrum.

"Just a minute, Harry," Senator McKellar, standing behind him, said, "let me introduce you." The microphones were on, and everyone in the building, and indeed across the nation, heard this homely and petulant little appeal to a very nervous President.

At last he was properly introduced. The new President then made his speech, pledging to carry on the war and peace policies of Franklin Delano Roosevelt. He ended with his customary modesty: "I ask only to be a good and faithful servant of my Lord and my people."

Before he set sail to meet with Stalin and Churchill, the new President executed one of the most important tasks of his life. He went to San Francisco to witness the signing of the Charter of the United Nations.

"The Charter of the United Nations," he told the delegates of many nations, gathered together for the momentous ceremony, ". . . is a solid structure upon which we can build a better world. Like this Charter, our Constitution came from a free and sometimes bitter exchange of conflicting opinions. When it was adopted no one regarded it as a perfect document. But it grew and developed and expanded. And upon it was built a bigger, a better, a more perfect union."

Truman had carried out the hopes and plans of Roosevelt. He urged the Congress to ratify the Charter. The world now had an organization designed to settle disagreements and to avoid future war. The war in Europe was drawing to a close. The world hoped that with the aid of the new organization —the United Nations—future catastrophes could be averted.

On June 16 Truman wrote to his mother and sister giving an outline of his busy schedule: ". . . and then [I] get ready to go to Berlin. How would you like to be the President des Etats Unis? It's a hell of a life.

"Love to you both.

Harry"

It *was* a hell of a life, as Truman was to find out in Potsdam.

As the surrender of Germany became imminent, Churchill grew more and more worried. It became evident that the Soviet Union had no intention of keeping the agreements it had signed at Yalta, the chief of which was that free elections would be held in the countries now occupied by Russia. Particularly in Poland, on whose behalf Great Britain had gone to war, Churchill had requested that there be Allied observers present at the election of a new Polish government, to guarantee the freedom of the ballot. The Soviet Union ignored the Yalta Agreement on this very special point.

Churchill, wise in political strategy and fearful of Soviet intentions, had called Truman to urge that American forces be kept in "the farthest advanced lines they had reached until we had been satisfied about Poland and other problems we had with the Russians."

But the peace arrangements for Germany drawn up by the Allies included a division into three separate zones, each administered by one of the three great powers, Russia, Great Britain, and the United States. Our troops already were in what had been designated as the Russian zone.

On June 4 Churchill for the second time urged that the American troops not be withdrawn to the American occupation zone.

"I view with profound misgivings," the British war leader said, "the retreat of the American Army to our line of occupation in the Central Sector, thus bringing Soviet power into the heart of Western Europe and *the descent of an iron curtain* between us and everything to the eastward." In a final plea to Truman, he added: "Nothing really important has been settled yet, and you and I will have to bear great responsibility for the future."

But Truman could not go back on America's pledge to the Soviet Union. He informed Churchill that the withdrawal of American troops from the Russian zone would begin on June 21.

Churchill was crushed. The presence of Russian troops in the heart of Europe, for the first time in history, "struck a knell" in his heart. "I sincerely hope," he wrote Truman, "that your action will in the long run make for a lasting peace in Europe."

It was the vain hope of a man who had been right in affairs of politics and strategy for many decades. The "iron curtain" descended in 1945. And the Potsdam Conference ushered in the cold war.

"Sometimes the end of a war means the beginning of trouble," Truman said. "I was thinking of that in July, 1945, after Germany surrendered, when I was on my way to Potsdam."

There were many problems to be solved at this first meeting between the new President and the old comrades in war, Stalin and Churchill. New national boundaries had to be settled, reparations had to be agreed upon, and the conduct of the war in the Pacific, which was still raging, had to be discussed.

Truman was also worried about a very human problem: two million starving, fearful people who had been caught behind the Russian advance on Berlin. They had to be fed. "Stalin said they didn't exist," Truman quotes the Generalissimo.

As the Russians rolled over Poland, Rumania, Bulgaria, Hungary, and Austria, they set up Communist governments, by force and by rigged elections, in each nation. This, of course, was in violation of the accord reached by Roosevelt, Churchill, and Stalin at Yalta. "Free elections" had been agreed upon. Stalin said the new Communist governments were "people's democracies," but the Soviets refused to allow British and American representatives into the new Communist countries. The conference at Potsdam was in the nature of a showdown. Stalin's attitude was noncommittal and his wry humor expressed his intransigence.

When Stalin demanded that the defeated German fleet be divided between the wartime allies, Churchill said: "Weapons of war are horrible things . . . the captured vessels should be sunk." Stalin insisted on dividing up the fleet, adding: "If Mr. Churchill wishes, he can sink his share."

As the conference proceeded, Truman became more and more discouraged with the atmosphere that appeared to exist between Churchill and Stalin. "They were willing to discuss anything, but not to decide. And I wanted decisions. I got impatient finally with all that bickering and said I was going to pack up and go home if we didn't settle something." Stalin laughed and said he was quite ready to go home, too.

On July 16, the day after he arrived at Potsdam, Truman received a message which was fateful for the whole world and for the future of mankind. The message read: "Babies satisfactorily born." Translated, this meant that the world's first atomic bomb had been successfully exploded at Alamogordo, New Mexico.

"On July 24," Truman writes, "I casually mentioned to Stalin that we had a new weapon of unusual destructive force. The Russian Premier showed no special interest. All he said was that he was glad to hear it and hoped the United States would make 'good use of it against the Japanese.' "

The reasons for this sanguine reaction to the momentous news became clear some weeks later, when Klaus Fuchs and David Greenglass were arrested. They had been selling American and British atomic secrets to the Soviets. Obviously, Stalin already knew about the development of the atomic bomb.


The Potsdam Conference continued with Clement Attlee in Churchill's chair when Churchill lost the British elections to the head of the Labor Party.

On July 30, President Truman wrote home to Grandview, Missouri:


"Dear Mama and Mary:
"The conference has been prolonged . . . You never saw such pig-headed people as are the Russians. I hope I never

have to hold another conference with them—but, of course, I will."

Then the son of Lamar, Grandview, and Independence, Missouri, goes on to say, almost in Mark Twain fashion:

"I will have to lunch with the English King aboard a British cruiser, and then he'll have to return the call to my ship, and then we'll sail for home. I'd rather fly . . . I could be home a week sooner. But they all yell their heads off when I talk of flying.

"I surely hope you are both well. Love to you both.

Harry"

The Potsdam Conference had kept the new President away from Washington for almost a month. Though several important decisions had been reached concerning the future shape of the world, the most important result of the conference was Truman's realization of what he himself had to do in molding future foreign policy. He had been through his baptism of fire in international relations, and whatever innocence he had once had about foreign affairs had vanished. The Mark Twainish "Innocent Abroad" returned to the United States with a policy already taking shape in his mind. He would not be "pushed around" by the Russians. Obviously, "the Russians were planning world conquest." American foreign policy from now on would be geared to this fact. America would frustrate Russian world domination whenever possible. As a result of the Potsdam Conference, Truman set the foreign policy of his country on the course it has followed for two decades. This policy is best expressed by George Kennan, one of the advisors to the government headed by Truman:

"It will be clearly seen that the Soviet pressure against the free institutions of the Western world is *something that can be contained* by the adroit and *vigilant application of counter-force* at a series of constantly shifting geographical and political points, corresponding to the shifts and maneuvers of Soviet policy . . . The Russians look forward to a duel of infinite duration . . ."

Truman girded himself for this duel. He was determined to *contain* the spreading ambitions of the Soviet Union.

# 8

Much had happened to the world, and to Truman, before he had left the United States for Potsdam. The Germans had surrendered unconditionally on May 8. On the day before V-E Day, the Trumans had moved from their temporary residence, Blair House, to the White House across the street.

Early on V-E Day, Truman wrote to his mother and sister:

"Dear Mama and Mary:

"I am sixty-one this morning, and I slept in the President's room in the White House last night. They have finished the painting and have some of the furniture in place. I'm hoping it will be ready for you by Friday.

"This will be a historical day. At 9 o'clock this morning I must make a broadcast to the country: announcing the German surrender . . ."

The President's daughter, then twenty-one, records the historic event in this fashion:

TUESDAY, MAY 8, 1945

We're still moving [into the White House]. My room is pink with antique white furniture. The bath . . . is enormous.

Her diary doesn't even mention the fact that the war in Europe is over. Obviously, moving day at home, as is only natural for a young girl, was a more exciting occasion. To her father it was "a solemn but glorious hour . . . I only wish that Franklin D. Roosevelt had lived to witness this day."

Though the war in Europe was over, the United States was up to its neck in the war in the Pacific. "The flags of freedom were flying all over Europe," but Japan had still to be vanquished.

When Truman, at the Potsdam Conference, heard news of the successful explosion of an atomic bomb in New

Mexico, he knew the surrender of Japan could not be far off. Atomic energy would deliver the knock-out blow.

Not until he became President of the United States did Truman even know of the existence of atomic energy.

"Once, when I was Senator and headed the War Investigating Committee, I started to look into the Manhattan Project where they were working on atomic energy, though I didn't know it.

"Henry Stimson, then Secretary of War, told me it was a very secret project and asked me not to investigate any further. Well, I knew he was a grand old man and a great American and I took his word for it."

Even when Truman became Vice-President, he was not told about the government's attempt to develop atomic energy. He, the second most important official in the government, had been kept in the dark. "When President Roosevelt died and I became President all of a sudden, I learned about our experiments with atomic energy for the first time."

Not until that day in Potsdam did Truman know that American scientists had been successful in harnessing the most powerful source of energy ever known. On that day, July 16, 1945, at 5:30 in the morning, a new age was born—the atomic age.

Now that Truman had knowledge of the successful testing of the atom bomb, he became a changed man.

"That news pepped me up tremendously. Up to this time,

in spite of our military and industrial power, we'd been sitting at Potsdam like a beggar with hat in hand. Not that we weren't a strong nation—we wanted help, to save as many of our boys' lives as possible. Now, we could negotiate from strength."

Winston Churchill immediately noticed the change in Truman's attitude. "He told the Russians just where they got on and off, and generally bossed the whole meeting."

The European war was practically over, but the war against Japan loomed as lasting for another two years, with the estimated loss of half a million American soldiers. Stalin had agreed to enter the Pacific war against Japan, but Truman said "he seemed to be stalling." "I knew," the President continued, "that if Stalin entered the war against Japan, he'd grab anything that wasn't tied down. Yet, my advisers insisted, we needed his help to save American lives."

Truman, however, feared that the arrival of Soviet troops in Japan would lead to the same results as were now evident in Europe. A trail of Communism led from Moscow to Berlin. Germany had been partitioned into an Allied and a Russian zone. Would the same thing now happen in Japan?

The United States had the atomic bomb. Would we use it against Japan?

The Japanese were fighting with a fanaticism unknown in the "long and lamentable" chronicle of war. Defeated Japanese officers committed hari-kari rather than surrender.

Their soldiers blew themselves up with hand grenades. Their kamikazi, or suicide squads, hurled themselves against American soldiers with primitive recklessness. The road to Tokyo had led from island to island, with thousands dead and wounded in the bloody advance across the blue Pacific. In Okinawa, says Truman, one out of three Americans ended up dead, wounded, or missing. "And we needed five million men to invade Kyushu, one of the principal islands of the Japanese mainland."

At Potsdam, knowing that the devastating atomic bomb was now in the American arsenal, Truman issued, on July 16, an ultimatum to Japan. He called on Japan to surrender. Twenty-seven million leaflets asking for the capitulation of Japan were dropped on the Japanese mainland. Radio appeals were broadcast continuously. Finally, the Japanese replied. They labeled the request "absurd."

There were only two atomic bombs in the American stockpile. They had to be used, if they were used at all, with the greatest "shock action." Four cities were chosen for possible bombing: Hiroshima, Kyoto, Niigata, and Nagasaki.

Secretary Stimson appealed to Truman not to bomb Kyoto, the ancient and venerated city which had once been the capital of Japan and was now a Japanese religious shrine.

The final choice of target was left to the Air Force. They would have to decide on the doomed city. Prevailing winds would be a vital factor in the choice. But it was Truman's decision, and Truman's alone, as Commander-in-Chief of the Armed Forces, to use the new bomb.

On a bright sunny morning in August, a B-29 force took off from the Pacific island of Tinian in the Marianas—its destination, Hiroshima. One of the planes, the *Enola Gay,* carried the concentrated ball of fire which scientists had wrenched from the forces of the universe.

At that very hour, Truman was on board the *Augusta,* returning from the Potsdam Conference.

"I was eating lunch with members of the crew when Captain Frank Graham . . . handed me the following message:

"To the President

"From the Secretary of War

"Big bomb dropped on Hiroshima August 5 at 7:15 P.M. Washington time.

"First reports indicate complete success . . ."

The success was so complete that literally, in a flash, the city was destroyed.

From the warship that was carrying him home, Truman told a horrified world: "It was to spare the Japanese people from utter destruction that the ultimatum of July 26 was issued at Potsdam. Their leaders promptly rejected that ultimatum. If they do not now accept our terms they may expect a rain of ruin from the air, the like of which has never been seen on this earth."

Nothing like the devastation wrought by that single blast over Hiroshima had ever been known by man. Man now had the capacity to harness elemental forces and hurl their power to destroy the world.

Still the Japanese would not surrender. On August 9, the second bomb was dropped on the city where Madam Butterfly had had her sad affair with her American sweetheart. Nagasaki was destroyed. Japan surrendered the next day.

Two days after the first blast, Stalin declared war against Japan and invaded Manchuria.

"The Soviets," said Truman, "hurried into Manchuria like a kid who's afraid he's going to be left out of a party."

"Our war against Japan was over," says Truman, "but our troubles with the Russians, as I anticipated, were not. In Manchuria they were still advancing five days after the Japanese had laid down their arms."

Stalin wished to be repaid for his unnecessary entry into the Japanese conflict. This was his opportunity to expand the power of the Soviets in the Far East as it had been expanded in Europe. He "wanted me to make him a present of the northern part of Hokkaido—one of the Japanese home islands. We refused. When Stalin couldn't squeeze anything out of me, he tried . . . working on General MacArthur [the Supreme Commander of the Allied Powers in Japan].

"The Soviets wanted MacArthur to set up separate Russian zones of influence in Japan . . . MacArthur told Stalin's General Antonov to go talk to me—and there the matter ended . . . They sulked and turned their efforts to propaganda for the Japanese Communist Party."

The morning after the bombing of Nagasaki, Japan surrendered. Atomic energy was now a factor in the life of man.

"The fact that we can release atomic energy," said Truman, "ushers in a new era in man's understanding of nature's forces. Atomic energy may in the future supplement the power that now comes from coal, oil and falling water . . . I shall . . . make further recommendations to the Congress as to how atomic power can become a powerful and forceful influence towards the maintenance of world peace."

Truman was not the father of the atomic age. Einstein, Fermi, Oppenheimer, and other scientists had made it possible for this new age to be born. But Truman, who alone had the power to order the use of the atomic bomb, must certainly go down in history as the godfather of the atomic age. And it was his job to deal with the terrible problems that arose from the new and awesome knowledge which had been given to man.

# 9

The President, and his wife Bess and their daughter Margaret, continued to live in the White House much as they had lived on North Delaware Street, Independence, Missouri. Truman was forever going around the White House checking windows and doors to see that they were locked for the night. Once in the middle of the night a thunderstorm came up, bringing torrential rains. Truman got up out of bed in his striped pajamas and padded around in bare feet to see if the rain was coming in. It was, and in buckets, around the windows. He ran to the bathroom, grabbed an armful of towels, and began mopping up. It did not cross the President's mind to call for help. When finally a servant appeared, he was horrified to see the President of the United States down on his hands and knees like a scrubwoman, or like any solicitous householder, trying to soak up the rain water before it did any damage.

Another time, in the midst of a family dinner, Truman playfully flipped a watermelon seed at Bess. "She responded in kind," says Margaret Truman, and "I joined the fray and we had a classic watermelon-seed fight at the table. In the middle of this battle one of the butlers came in to remove the plates, but retreated in short order, in a rain of melon seeds." The other servants, safe behind the swinging door which led to the pantry, goggled at the Trumans for a moment, then bent double with laughter. There had never been folks like the Trumans in the White House before.

One day the President asked his aged mother and his sister to visit him at the White House for a Mother's Day weekend. She was flown from Missouri to Washington in the Presidential plane, *Sacred Cow*. Roosevelt had used the plane, and because of his crippled legs, an elevator had been installed in the plane. When they landed in Washington, Martha Truman tried using it and it got stuck.

After being rescued, she turned to the pilot and said, "I'm going to tell Harry that this plane is no good and I could walk just as easily as I could ride."

Truman and the inevitable reporters were at the airport to greet the old lady. "Oh, fiddlesticks," she said, "why didn't you tell me there was going to be all this fuss, and I wouldn't have come."

Old Martha Truman, whose family had fought on the Confederate side in the Civil War and who had come to loathe the name Abraham Lincoln, was afraid she would have to sleep in the bed Lincoln had slept in. She had heard, from her son Vivian, that it was the only available bed in the White House. "You tell Harry, if he puts me in the room with Lincoln's bed in it, I'll sleep on the floor."

As it was, she was given the Rose Room, where visiting queens stay. "My mother took one look at the bed," Truman reports, "and started walking around the room. This was not for her. The bed was too high and too big, and the surroundings were too fussy."

The little old lady opened a door and peered into the adjoining room, used by ladies-in-waiting. It was much smaller and had a regular-size single bed in it.

"This is where I'm going to sleep," she announced.

"She did not seem to think there was anything special about my being in the White House or about my being President," her son said. "She thought it was just the natural thing. It did not give her any ideas of grandeur. She was," says her son, "just the same Mama she had always been."

And he was the same son *he* had always been—and the same kind of man.

History, in the early months of Truman's presidency, was being made with the speed of a cannonball. There had been the formation of the United Nations, the surrender of Germany, the Potsdam Conference—that wellspring of so much that happened in the postwar world. There had been the birth of the atomic age, and the surrender of Japan. All this happened within ninety days. Truman had not only carried out the policies and plans of his predecessor; he also attempted to solve the problems which they brought. He, in a manner of speaking, had been the voice and soul of the deceased F.D.R. for ninety days.

A few weeks after the end of hostilities around the globe, Truman sent a message to Congress. "September 6, 1945, is the date that symbolizes for me my assumption of the office of President *in my own right*. It was on that day and with this message that I first spelled out the details of the program of liberalism and progressivism which was to be the foundation of my administration."

Roosevelt's program had been called the New Deal. Truman's program would be called the Fair Deal.

Again, Truman's mind went back to the conference table at Potsdam. It was at Potsdam that he learned Stalin's strategy. Stalin was convinced that the United States would make the same mistakes after World War II as it had after World War I. He was certain that the United States would fall into an economic depression, and depression was the breeding ground for Communism. Already in Italy the Communists had grown powerful, and in France, and in other European countries. Stalin had but to wait to take over Europe—and perhaps the United States. There was a fiercely loyal (loyal to the Soviet Union) Communist Party of the United States, with a membership of over a million dedicated men and women.

"We had won the war. But there was a serious question whether we would survive the peace," Truman mused.

American factories had been going full speed for four years, turning out war material. Now these factories were to stop production. Millions of men and women would be thrown out of work. Millions of soldiers would be returning home and they would need jobs.

During the Potsdam Conference, on a tour of the devastated city of Berlin nearby, Truman had put into words his vision of "a world in which *ALL* the people will have the opportunity to enjoy the good things of life—and not just a few at the top."

At home, after four years of war, there were all kinds of shortages—from pots and pans to lawn mowers. Food was plentiful—American harvests had been abundant—but now this food would be needed to feed the peoples of ravaged Europe.

The problem was how to convert the economy of the United States from an economy geared for war to one geared for peace, and to do so without a depression. Truman sent his "Fair Deal" message to Congress four days after the proclamation of V-J Day. The message caused an uproar among the people who believed Truman represented the conservative element in the Democratic Party.

Judge Rosenman, who helped prepare the message, stated:

"History will record that he—that his administration—was as liberal as any we've had in the United States."

When a Republican member of Congress read Truman's message, he fumed: "Not even President Roosevelt asked for so much at one sitting . . . it is just a plain case of out-new-dealing the New Deal."

"All I asked for," said Truman, "were those things which I knew were necessary if the United States was to compete successfully with Stalin's International Communism for the minds and loyalties of our people."

Among other things, the Fair Deal message asked Congress for speedy action on full-employment legislation based on the cooperation of industry, agriculture, and labor. It asked for health insurance and prepaid medical care; for the development of a St. Lawrence seaway project; for federal aid to education. And it demanded equal opportunity for all, regardless of race, religion, *or color*.

The Full-Employment Act of 1946 made it the responsibility of the federal government to "co-ordinate and utilize all its plans, functions and resources" not only to *achieve* full employment but to *maintain* it. Millions of men and women were reentering the labor market after four years of working in war plants. The change-over to a peacetime economy had to be accomplished with as few lay-offs as possible. Also, millions of soldiers were being demobilized and had to find jobs. The task was enormous.

Not only were the needs of Americans clamoring for attention, but a devastated Europe was crying for help. The call was urgent in Germany, France, Belgium, Italy—especially for coal. Truman was aware of the coal famine. "Unless large quantities of coal are made available to liberated Europe in forthcoming months," he wrote to Churchill, "there is grave danger of . . . political and economic chaos." And to Stalin he said, "An acute coal famine threatens Europe this winter . . . despite our own shortage of coal . . . we are now shipping coal to Europe as an emergency measure . . ."

At home, meanwhile, there was growing labor unrest. Two major strikes threatened the shaky economy of the United States, endangering also the struggling economy of postwar Europe.

In the spring of 1946, when John L. Lewis of the United Mine Workers, and Alvanley Johnston of the Railroad Trainman, pulled out coal mines and railroads on strike, Truman said, "They were hurting a hundred and fifty million other people in this country and God knows how many more in Europe."

Truman was the kind of President who did not pussyfoot. When he hit, he hit hard. Always he used a small-town understanding of, and approach to, the large domestic and foreign issues. He once compared Stalin with Tom Pendergast, the Kansas City political boss.

Truman seemed to be saying, "Well, this is the way I would solve it if I were back home in Missouri." What is remarkable is that this attitude worked.

"I had to get those mines and railroads running again,"

Truman said, "even if it meant breaking the strikes. All my life I've fought for the rights of the workingman. But no one has a right to put his interests above his country." And then he did the typically courageous thing. He was willing to lay his political future on the line. "I had come into office with Labor's support, but I had to stand up against them now, even if it cost me my political career."

Truman ordered the coal mines—privately owned property—seized by the federal government.

He also called the heads of the striking railroad unions to the White House and told them: "If you think I'm going to sit here and let you tie up this country, you're crazy as hell. I'm going to protect the public and you're going to run those railroads, and you can put that in your pipe and smoke it."

The labor leaders put what the President said into their pipes and they smoked it. But they denounced him as the nation's number-one strikebreaker. They called him a Fascist and vowed to defeat Truman when and if he should ever run for office again.

John L. Lewis, the head of the mineworkers, said that Truman was a man "totally unfitted for his position. He is a malignant, scheming sort of individual who is dangerous not only to the United Mine Workers but dangerous to the United States of America."

"I never minded what people said about me," Truman once remarked. "My feeling is, if you can't stand the heat, get out of the kitchen."

For Truman, the kitchen at that moment happened to be

the White House and the Presidential desk at which he sat. Prominent on that desk was a printed sign reading: "The Buck Stops Here." In other words, people could "pass the buck," but when it reached the President's office, he was responsible for it. Truman accepted this responsibility with alacrity. It was as if he now remembered those early days when as a bank clerk he complained, "I have nothing to decide." He had plenty to decide now. But when, in the Congressional elections of that year, the Democrats were soundly beaten, Senator Fulbright suggested that Truman ought to resign and let Congress put in a Republican President.

"I wasn't about to do that," Truman remarked laconically.

But he had made it clear "that Labor and Management were partners in business, and neither can do without the other." From his small-town experience in Missouri, he had observed that "when partners squabble, business goes to pot. And when they're fair and square with each other, they're both better off."

It was this simple philosophy which he applied to labor-management problems when he became President. In the field of international affairs, the world was to be startled by a similar simplicity of approach. In Europe the Communists were on the move. Truman had to act quickly and he had to act decisively.

# 10

The emergence of a foreign policy which was distinctly Truman's own and which may stamp him as one of our great Presidents begins with the problem he had to face in postwar Greece.

"Even when I was a boy," Truman says, "with my head in every history book in Independence, Missouri, I learned a lesson about Greece. It's not even as big as the state of Missouri, but Greece left us ideas that never died . . ."

One of these ideas was the freedom of the individual, and this became one of the cornerstones of the glory that was

Greece. When Truman became President, this freedom, which had been throttled during the Nazi occupation of Greece, was again being threatened, this time by civil war. The Communists were using the prostrate country as a battlefield. They were determined to form a Soviet-type state in the shadows of the Parthenon. The counterattack was led by a reactionary faction that had all the earmarks of Fascism. The British were trying to restore order in Greece, but now, in 1947, they served notice to the United States that Great Britain could no longer give economic and military aid to the stricken country. They were about to withdraw.

Truman knew that the Soviets would move swiftly to fill the vacuum. At that very moment the Communists were putting pressure on Greece's neighbor, Turkey. If Stalin was successful in these moves, the whole Mediterranean area would be in danger of falling under Russian domination. To the north and west of Greece lay the already Communist countries of Bulgaria and Albania. These countries were shipping arms to Greece. A full-fledged war was about to break out.

"That year, when it was springtime in Greece, no one was planting for a harvest. Greek kids were dying of hunger while the adults were killing each other. The Right and the Left were at each other's throats. And the Russians felt they were holding all the cards, but waited to see what *we* would do."

This was the President's summary of the situation that led

to the remarkable declaration known as the "Truman Doctrine."

Here were two countries, Greece and Turkey, three thousand miles from American shores, being challenged by Soviet Power.

"It was time for decision," said Truman, "and courage to make it." He was determined to send help to the people of Greece. But would the Soviets go to war if the United States opposed them? Today the question may seem academic. But in 1946 and 1947, this was the first great confrontation of the two leading powers of the world.

On March 12, 1947, Harry S Truman stood before a joint session of Congress and said in his flat, unadorned Missouri voice:

"I believe that it must be the policy of the United States to support free peoples who are resisting attempted subjugation by armed minorities or by outside pressures. I believe that we must assist free peoples to work out their own destinies in their own way."

He then asked Congress for $400 million to aid Greece and Turkey.

The nation was astounded. This was a complete break with the traditional foreign-policy posture of the United States since the days of George Washington. The first President had warned against "foreign entanglements," and the Monroe Doctrine had echoed the warning. Now the United States was being led into a new phase of its development by the thirty-third President. She now admitted that she was part of, and concerned for, the free peoples of the world, wherever they were.

On April 5, 1947, Truman declared: "We must take a positive stand. It is no longer enough to say, 'We don't want war.' We must act in time—ahead of time—to stamp out the smoldering beginnings of any conflict that may threaten to spread over the world."

The Truman Doctrine, uttered two years after the close of World War II, has remained the basis of American policy to this day. America had shed forever its traditional isolationism. But more—the Monroe Doctrine proclaimed, in 1823, that European powers "coveting the territory of existing governments in Latin America" were warned not to commit acts of aggression in this hemisphere. Now came the sequel to the Monroe Doctrine, the Truman Doctrine. Our aid was extended to freedom-loving peoples anywhere, around the globe.

"People were telling me [apropos the Truman Doctrine] —that was the job of the United Nations," Truman said. "As if I didn't know. But the United Nations didn't have that kind of power and respect in 1947."

Truman was attacked by the Left, represented by Henry A. Wallace, who had been Roosevelt's Vice-President and, but for fate, would now have been President. Wallace said, "In proposing this reckless adventure Truman is betraying the great tradition of America and the leadership of the great American who preceded him."

And Senator Robert Taft, spokesman of the conservative

Right, predicted equal disaster as the result of the Truman Doctrine.

Nevertheless, Truman's policy was accepted by the Congress. Now he needed a plan by which to navigate the new course the United States had taken under his leadership.

"What is Europe now?" Winston Churchill asked, and then replied, "It is a rubble heap . . . a charnel house . . . a breeding ground of pestilence and hate."

Europe was ripe for Communism, and Stalin was making rapid progress.

"What I needed," said Truman, "was what you might call a plan for a plan. I had to figure out a way for the Communist-threatened countries to pull themselves up by their own bootstraps."

His Secretary of State, a man of enormous prestige whom Truman greatly admired, was George Catlett Marshall, General of the Army. Truman met with Marshall and the State Department advisers.

"If I was going to keep free nations of Europe from trading their freedom for food and coal, I needed a plan— yesterday!" said Truman.

The President was to make a speech on May 8, hinting at the outlines of the plan. On that day his mother became seriously ill, and Truman handed his speech to Undersecretary of State Dean Acheson and asked him to deliver it for him.

In Cleveland, Mississippi, Dean Acheson gave the world

the first outlines of what was to be known as the Marshall Plan. The United States, Acheson said, must "push ahead with the reconstruction of the great workshops of Europe. Free peoples who are seeking to preserve their independence and democratic institutions and human freedoms against totalitarian pressures, either internal or external, will receive top priority for *American reconstruction aid.*"

Never before in the history of the world had a victor been willing to restore the vanquished. That is what Truman's message, delivered by the Undersecretary of State, meant to America and to the world.

The speech got scant attention from the American press, but in England and on the Continent it was widely reported.

On May 23, the Policy Planning Staff of the State Department at last submitted its proposals to General Marshall. The details of the plan of action were just what President Truman had hoped for—"a program of economic rehabilitation for Western European nations as a bulwark against Communism."

General Marshall was to deliver the Commencement Day address at Harvard. He was not enthusiastic about revealing the great American plan at a college commencement. He thought the message might be ignored by the press.

"But," says Truman, "I told Marshall to go ahead and make it! I had to send up a trial balloon sooner or later." He knew that he would have to get Congress to vote tremendous sums of money to get the plan launched.

"If the Big Idea was going to fall flat on its budget, at least the thud would stand less chance of being detected by the all-too-sensitive Congressional seismograph."

The Big Idea was simple. The European countries were to meet and draw up a recovery program *for themselves*. The United States would furnish not only the money, but food, medical supplies, machinery, and clothes. The cost? Seventeen billion dollars!

The Marshall Plan as outlined in the speech at Harvard drew immediate world-wide attention. Devastated Europe began to breathe the air of hope. But in Congress the staggering cost of the Plan sent a shudder through the marble corridors. One Senator said "Truman thought it was best to keep it quiet that the Marshall Plan was his own idea, so he made it appear that it was entirely Marshall's doing because Marshall was popular with Congress."

The European nations met to draw up a plan for their own recovery. The Soviets, fearful of the efficacy of the Plan, refused to join the conference. If Europe recovered, with American aid, the new breeding ground for Communism would be stamped out. Moscow made its satellites Czechoslovakia and Poland withdraw from the conference, too.

Congress balked at voting the staggering sum.

"But," says Truman, "I pointed out that money spent over a period of four years to rebuild a decent standard of living would amount to only 5 percent of what it had cost us to defeat the Axis."

And he goes on to say: "I pointed out again and again

that indefinite Communist expansion could only mean an all-out atomic war."

In March the Senate finally passed the Marshall Plan by a resounding majority of sixty-nine to seventeen.

Truman was convinced that he had won the first round in the battle to keep Europe free. But Stalin was not just standing by. The Soviets were on the move.

# 11

The chosen field of battle was Berlin—symbol of Russia's penetration into the heart of Europe—symbol of British and American determination to have a say in the shaping of postwar Europe. Berlin, under the terms of the peace agreement, had been divided into Russian, British, American, and French zones. It was (and is) an unnatural and unwieldy manner of governing a great city—a former capital of a nation. Access into West Berlin and the American zone was through the Russian-controlled zone, by river, railroad, Autobahn, or any of three narrow air corridors. West

Berlin was, and is, an island surrounded by Communist territory.

On April 1, 1948, the Russians sealed off all highway, rail, and river traffic in and out of Berlin. "Technical difficulties" was given as the reason. No food, no supplies could come in. It was the opening shot in a war that was actually the Russian response to the Marshall Plan and the Truman Doctrine.

Moscow had quickly realized that the mighty weapon for Democracy represented by the Marshall Plan would threaten the spreading power of Communism. If the Russians could force the Americans out of West Berlin, the Marshall Plan, the Truman Doctrine, and indeed the prestige of America would be made a mockery. Berlin was chosen as the scene of confrontation because it was the most advantageous battlefield for the Russians. It was Russia who determined who would and who would not enter West Berlin, since, Moscow believed, West Berlin—showcase of democracy at work—existed only by sufferance of the Communist authorities.

The Marshall Plan was the opening salvo in the cold war, which at any moment threatened to become a hot one.

"Our policy," Marshall had said, "is not directed against any country or doctrine, but against hunger, poverty, desperation, and chaos."

This kind of talk, and the economic aid that America was giving, immensely weakened Russia's posture as "champion of the masses." Here was a capitalist country coming to the rescue of a devastated Europe. Everyone knew that as Russian troops advanced across border after border, the conquered countries had been looted of machinery and all means of production. Tools, indeed whole factories, were sent back to a devastated Russia. The Soviets hoped to rebuild their own economy quickly and then supply the rest of Europe with goods, and Communism. But the United States was getting there first, with goods and democracy.

Russia fought the Marshall Plan with various weapons. At first she tried, and succeeded, in spreading panic in Berlin by flooding the city with worthless money that could buy little or nothing. Inflation followed.

Truman counterattacked by ordering the American zone to issue its own currency. The people knew that the West German mark was reliable, and the black market disappeared. The Russians became incensed. On June 24 all routes between the West and Berlin were sealed. A message came from Moscow that the Western Powers had no right to be in Berlin at all. Here was stalemate: two powers, allies only a few years before, facing each other now as mortal enemies. Russia needed a victory somewhere; she had suffered setbacks in Italian and French elections, and Tito in Yugoslavia was showing his independence of Moscow. The Marshall Plan, it was evident, constituted a major attack on Communism. It would succeed in putting Europe back on its feet. Russia needed a victory, and Berlin appeared to be the easiest site to gain one. Stalin was willing, through starvation, to destroy thousands of men, women, and children to gain his victory.

In the White House, President Truman was asked point-blank: "Are we going to stay in Berlin or not?" Truman's reply was equally point-blank: "We are going to stay. Period."

But "many thoughts went through my mind," Truman said. "How does a city blockaded from the rest of the world survive? Where does food come from? Medicines? Coal for heat, and the making of electric power? And what about milk? I was told six thousand newborn babies would die."

On the day that the blockade of Berlin became total, June 24, 1948, the Republican Convention nominated its candidate for President in the elections that would be held in the fall. He was Thomas E. Dewey, who had previously run against Roosevelt. He was sure to win. Truman, by his aggressive policies, had become unpopular with large blocs of powerful elements in the United States. He was not sure whether he ought to run. His mother had said to reporters in Grandview, when she learned that her son had suddenly become President: "I can't really be glad he's President, because I'm sorry that President Roosevelt is dead. *If Harry had been voted in,* I'd be out waving a flag . . ."

"If Harry had been voted in!" Truman wondered if he ought to run against a man everybody conceded was a winner even before the election. It was the crisis over Berlin that helped Truman make up his mind to run. The situation in Europe was critical. War threatened. He had to remain in authority to make his national and foreign policies work. He was determined to run against Dewey. He was determined to win.

"But," he says, "the Berlin crisis was uppermost in my mind. Europe watched and waited to see what I would do. America watched and waited to see what I would do. And the Kremlin waited. I knew that my decision about Berlin would be loaded with risk—the risk of a Third World War."

On the following day, the twenty-fifth of June, Truman summoned his Cabinet to discuss the Berlin crisis. Some members favored using armored trains to smash through the Russian blockade and bring food and supplies to the beleaguered city. Others suggested embarking on a "preventive war."

In his diary of those desperately tense days, Truman wrote: "I have a terrible feeling that we are very close to war."

The President conferred with his generals. He wondered what risks would be involved if the United States attempted to supply Berlin by armed convoys. The generals thought the Russians would meet the convoys with armed force.

General Hoyt Vanderberg advised the President against sending more planes to the Berlin area. He was afraid that, should we become involved in war, the United States would need the planes to protect our shores and outposts.

"I did not agree with the General," says Truman. "We had to take chances. We had to take risks. You think about a lot of things before you make a decision like that—about American boys getting killed, about an atom bombing. I came to my decision. We would stay in Berlin, come hell or high water. We would fly in the supplies right over East Germany into West Berlin."

Truman had taken on the Russian challenge. He ordered planes from Guam, from Alaska, from Tokyo, Hawaii, Texas, and California to proceed immediately to the "Berlin Front." The Berlin airlift, which was to arouse the admiration of the free world, began. Food and supplies were flown into West Berlin via the narrow air corridor. The people of West Berlin were being fed. They were being clothed. They were receiving medical supplies. Even more impressive was their new spirit. They were defiant—at war, without guns, with the Russians.

Meanwhile, in Philadelphia, on July 13, Truman was nominated to run for the Presidency. He had earned the right to do so by his own actions and his willpower. But it was almost unanimously agreed that the man from Missouri had little chance of beating Dewey in November. Even the Democrats were certain he would be swamped by a Republican victory. Signs appeared at the Democratic Convention: "We're just mild about Harry." The *New York Post* said: "The Party might as well immediately concede the election to Dewey and save the wear and tear of campaigning."

Harry Truman was never one to concede defeat. He set out on a whirlwind, whistle-stopping campaign. All the while, he kept in touch with the ominous Berlin situation.

"There was always the danger that a trigger-happy Russian pilot might create an incident that would ignite the powder keg," Truman said. "And who could trust Stalin? The old so-and-so would make agreements one day and break them the next day!"

Truman was convinced that, barring accidents, his firmness with Stalin would keep America out of war. He was determined to remain President.

"I don't want you to vote for me," he told a crowd of workers in Grand Rapids, Michigan, "I want you to get out on election day and vote for yourselves—for your interests."

And in Detroit his speech had evangelical fervor. "We are in a hard, tough fight against shrewd and rich opponents . . . [but] . . . I know that we are going to win this crusade for the right."

Then he began to "give 'em hell." He began to "mow 'em down."

In Dexter, Iowa, he spoke to 75,000 people, mostly farmers. "I can plow a straight furrow," he said. "A prejudiced witness said so—my mother." He recounted his life on the family farm with four mules and a gangplow, "not the tractor of the modern era." The farmers stomped and hollered their approval. Harry Truman, fighting for his political life, moved on across the country. The language he used had never before been heard in a Presidential campaign. He called the Republicans "gluttons of privilege" and "bloodsuckers with offices in Wall Street." Unmercifully, he castigated "the no-good, do-nothing" Republican Congress.

The crowds ate it up. The Republican candidate Thomas E. Dewey, confident, polished, and somewhat pompous, campaigned as though he had already won. All he need do was maintain the lead every poll in the country showed he had. But Truman appeared confident that the people would vote him in. There were few who shared his confidence. Even Bess Truman asked a friend, "Does he really believe that he'll be elected?"

In Berlin the Russian reaction to the Allied airlift was awaited with apprehension. Would they retaliate with war? Then one day "the Russians announced that they would hold air maneuvers in a general area that included the airlanes used by our airlift," Truman says. "I was filled with dread, foreboding. The mighty Russian air force running interference against our planes. This was the spark which could blow us all to hell."

Truman, however, told the Russians that the airlift would go on. He "was plenty worried, but there was no backing out now."

Berlin had become a symbol of America's and the West's dedication to the cause of freedom.

Meanwhile, election day in America arrived at last.

"Most of the newsmen," Margaret Truman reports, "seemed convinced that Dewey was going to win. One reporter . . . said he felt the people of the United States were in the mood to give Harry Truman anything in the world he wanted—except the Presidency."

On the week the election was held, *Life* featured a photo of Dewey and his wife aboard a small boat. The caption read: *"The next President* travels by ferry boat . . ."

Truman, on his way back to his home town, Independence, to vote, said: "We have told the people the truth, and the people are with us. The *people* are going to win this election!"

Margaret Truman writes in her diary:

NOV. 1, 1948

The campaign is all over. Now we wait until tomorrow is done to see how the voters decide. We can take whatever comes, but I wonder if the country can.

TUESDAY, NOV. 2, 1948

We voted at 10 o'clock. It looks like a big vote.

*Later:* What a night. I haven't been to bed at all. We are ahead, but at about 1:30 A.M. we hit a slump.

Dewey's victory statement was expected at 9 P.M. The first returns showed that Truman was leading, however. Even Jim Farley, the political sage of the Democratic Party, went on the radio to say: "But this is only an early lead. He cannot win—his early lead will fold up."

Truman said, "I'm going to bed."

Margaret reports in her diary: "Dad has slipped away to

Excelsior Springs [to sleep] and the reporters are going crazy trying to find him."

Harry Truman recalls that night in his terse, laconic manner: "The boys told me once in a while—they'd wake me and tell me there was something to report on the thing. At six o'clock I was defeated. At ten o'clock I was defeated. Four o'clock I had won the election."

It was perhaps the most exciting election in the country's history. Millions of Americans had gone to bed certain that their next President was Thomas E. Dewey. They woke up to find that the man from Missouri had been elected President in his own right and by his own Herculean efforts.

"Wednesday, Nov. 3, 1948," Margaret writes in her diary: "We have won! I still can't believe it is all over and over so well. I am packing frantically and the phone is ringing madly. There was no celebration planned in Independence and they suddenly got one together and the entire square around the Courthouse was jam-packed with 20,000 friends and relatives and neighbors. We've known most of them for years. It was really very touching. I heard the news that Dewey had conceded while uptown when all the bells in the town went crazy and I thought that somebody had short-circuited them."

It has been reported that Dewey "was in a state of shock. He admitted later that he felt like the man who had awakened inside a coffin with a lily in his hand and said to himself, 'If I'm alive, what am I doing here? And if I'm dead, why do I have to go to the bathroom?'"

The day after the election, the President was handed an early edition of the *Chicago Tribune*. The headline screamed: *Dewey Defeats Truman.*

"That's one for the books," Truman laughed.

Some Republicans were furious at "the trick that had been played on them."

"I don't care how the thing is explained," grumbled Senator Taft. "It defies all common sense to send that roughneck ward politician back to the White House."

The people obviously wanted the "roughneck ward politician" back in the White House.

"You've got to give the little man credit," a more generous-minded Republican Senator remarked. "There he was, flat on his back. Everyone had counted him out, but he came up fighting and won the battle. That's the kind of courage the American people admire." The statement summed up what the majority of the American people obviously felt.

Harry Truman remarked laconically on his return to the White House: "There was much work to be done, and I was eager to get on with it." First on the schedule was the Berlin crisis, which was now reaching a climax.

On November 30, the Soviet leaders caused a split on the Berlin City Council—the nominal governing body of the city. For all practical purposes, the city was divided in two just as surely as if a wall had been built between what we now know as East Berlin and West Berlin. A new identification system was put into effect, making it almost impossible to maintain contacts between the eastern and western parts of the city.

The serious threat of war made Truman present the Berlin crisis to the Security Council of the young United Nations.

"We wanted a settlement," Truman said, "but we could not accept a settlement that would put the people of Berlin at the mercy of the Soviets and their German Communist hirelings."

The United States, prodded by the dogged and unyielding man from Independence, had fought off and beaten back, by means of a remarkable and dangerous airlift, all Russian attempts to force us out of Berlin.

The men in the Kremlin began to realize that, short of a shooting war, their efforts to force the United States out of Berlin were doomed.

It became apparent to the nations of Europe that some system had to be set up—a system of mutual military aid—to ward off Russia's growing "toughness and truculence." Ultimately this led to the formation of NATO—the North Atlantic Treaty Organization.

Abruptly, the Russians began to back down when they realized the determination of the Western Allies to defend themselves against Soviet aggression.

On May 12, the Russians suddenly lifted the blockade of Berlin. But, because of the military pact known as NATO, the Red Army was ordered "to maintain combat preparations on a high level."

For his part, Truman "was determined to see to it that the Soviets understood that we were firmly committed to the defense of Western Europe, that their days of land-grabbing, of nation-grabbing were over."

# 12

"We were living in chaos at home," Margaret Truman records, "—the [White] House was about to fall in." This is a literal and accurate statement of fact. The weary old structure was collapsing. "Dad went upstairs," she continues, "and found that my Steinway piano had fallen through the floor. A large hole had opened up in the second floor and the piano was sitting there tipsily, with one leg in the hole."

The engineers were summoned. After a thorough investigation, it was discovered that the whole White House had to be braced. To the Trumans it was a wonder that the cherished building hadn't fallen down around their ears. The entire inner structure would have to be removed, right down to the bare shell of the outer walls. Within those outer walls, a new White House would have to be erected. The renovation would take a year, at least. So once again the Trumans moved to Blair House.

The Secret Service men guarding the President were worried. Not only was Blair House directly on the street, but Truman's bedroom on the second floor looked out over it. An assassin could in fact toss a bomb through the window.

Actually, while the Trumans were residing at Blair House, an attempt *was* made to assassinate the President. He was taking a nap after lunch. Two Puerto Rican nationalists, who believed that their native island should not have commonwealth status but should be independent, arrived intending to kill the President. The Secret Service men stopped them at the entrance to Blair House. The Nationalists whipped out guns. Shots were exchanged. In the confusion, one of the assassins raced for the front door. He was shot down by the Secret Service men as he climbed the second step, but a White House policeman was killed in the exchange of fire.

Truman, hearing the gunfire, jumped out of bed and ran to the window to see what was going on.

"Damn it, get back!" a guard shouted. "Get back!"

Truman was calm and went about his scheduled appointments after the fracas had died down.

"A President has to expect these things," he remarked.

"The only thing you have to worry about is bad luck. I never had bad luck."

Every day Truman got up at 5:30 in the morning and put in a day of sixteen or eighteen hours. His early days as a farmer still had an influence on the President. He was a fiend on weather forecasting. The Weather Bureau sent him daily temperature and rainfall charts, and he delighted in studying them.

He hated snobs. He met Lady Astor once. She was born and bred in Virginia but had gone to England to live and there had acquired a British accent. At their meeting, she made fun of Truman's flat, Missouri twang. Truman snorted: "At least my accent is an honest one." The Lady was promptly put in her place.

He had a habit of scribbling his opinions of visitors who came to see him in the Presidential office.

"This man," he once scrawled on a piece of paper while the visitor talked on and on, "not only wants to run the country but the universe and the entire milky way."

His comment on another visitor is short and incisive: "Boloney peddler," he wrote.

He had dinner either alone or with his family at seven o'clock. Once he wrote derisively in his diary: "I take a hand-bath in the finger bowl and go back to work. What a life."

For all the killing pace of his office, he found time to read—he is an expert on historical battles; he found time to play the piano, which he had learned to play as a boy; and he found time to follow his daughter's career as a singer—once to the amazement and amusement of the entire nation.

Margaret had given a song recital in Washington which her proud father attended. She was panned by one of the critics. Here is an extract from Truman's diary.

"Margie held a concert here in D.C. on Dec. 5th. It was a good one.

"A frustrated critic on the Washington Post wrote a lousy review. The only thing, General Marshall said, he didn't criticize was the varnish on the piano."

The irate father wrote a blistering letter to the critic. The fact that you were President didn't mean that you stopped being a father.

"I wrote him what I thought of him. I told him he was lower than Mr. X and that was intended to be an insult worse than the reflection on his ancestry. I would never reflect on a man's mother, because mothers are not to be attacked, although mine was.

"I've been accused of putting my baby, who is the apple of my eye, in a bad position. I don't think that is so. She doesn't either—thank the Almighty."

This is the actual letter the angry Papa Truman wrote:

"I have just read your lousy review buried in the back pages. You sound like a frustrated man that never made a success, an eight-ulcer man on a four-ulcer job, and all four ulcers working.

"I never met you, but if I do you'll need a new nose and plenty of beefsteak and perhaps a supporter below. Westbrook Pegler, a guttersnipe, is a gentleman compared to you. You can take that as more of an insult than a reflection on your ancestry."

Margaret says that, as a family, "we had a code, which was to do the right thing, do it the best we could, never complain and never take advantage. When my father became President our code did not change."

There is a letter Truman sent to his daughter that not only illustrates the family code but has the quality of a Missouri Polonius's advice to his son Laertes.

"Dear Margie," Truman wrote from his White House office, "It was a most happy week-end. It always is when you are with your Mommy and Daddy. Your Pop has been carefully watching the progress and change in his daughter, just as he watched it from five to fifteen. You've never had any advice from your Dad except in your interests . . . I want you to succeed in whatever you undertake. To do that you must give it all you have. Keep your balance and display all the Truman-Wallace mulishness where right and wrong are in the balance. Right must always prevail. Do not let glamor get you. There are decent, honorable people among the very rich, just as there are among the very poor. Honor knows no class. It is just as great and as necessary at one end of the scale as at the other. No one can say which is the top. Jesus Christ was the son of a carpenter (foster son) and was one himself. He was looked down upon by the socially great of his time. So were Martin Luther, John Knox, Wycliffe, Thomas Jefferson, Andrew Jackson and Abraham Lincoln.

"Remember always to keep your balance no matter how great you may become in your own time. Great men and women are assayed in future generations. Your Dad will never be reckoned among the great but you can be sure he did his level best and gave all he had to his country. There is an epitaph in Boothill Cemetery in Tombstone, Arizona, which reads, 'Here lies Jack Williams; he done his damnedest.' What more can a person do? I hope that will be yours and your Dad's epitaph.

"Love,
Dad"

# 13

"I am determined," said President Truman, "that the United States should be secure. I am equally determined that we shall keep our historic liberties."

He believed that "our historic liberties" were being threatened at home while he waged the fight to extend liberty and freedom abroad. In 1947 he asserted: "As Americans we believe that every man should be free to live his life as he wishes. He should be limited only by his responsibility to his fellow countrymen. If this freedom is to be more than a dream, each man must be guaranteed equality of opportunity. The only limit to an American's achievement should be his ability, his industry and his character."

He called for the abolition of segregation and discrimination. He called for federal protection against lynching. He called for a law to guard the right for citizens—*all* citizens—to vote.

"I had to give meaning to such phrases as 'All men are created equal'—it didn't make any difference whether he was a Jew, Protestant, Catholic or Negro—he had a right to the protection of what the Constitution guarantees." Truman told his Attorney-General that it was his duty to see that equality before the law was accorded to every citizen of the United States, regardless of race, creed, or color.

"The Attorney-General thought I was hipped on the subject," Truman remarks. "I admitted that I was and I still am." He once said, long before he was President: "I believe in the brotherhood of man, not merely the brotherhood of white men, but the brotherhood of all men before law. I believe in the Constitution and the Declaration of Independence. In giving the Negroes the rights which are theirs, we are only acting in accord with our own ideals of a true democracy." When he came into power, this credo became a living thing.

Truman, as Commander-in-Chief of the Armed Forces, took the first, long, practical step toward integration. He ordered the Armed Forces to integrate. Negro soldiers and white soldiers would share mess halls, recreation halls, and living quarters. They would share life together just as they would share danger and death together on the battlefields. Not since Abraham Lincoln had any President of the United States issued such a revolutionary order for equality and justice.

"I realized," Truman commented, "that this first step would be a long, long march in the uphill fight for civil rights. I also knew that it might also be a march over my political grave. But that didn't count with me."

The uproar that followed his executive order declaring that there shall be equality of treatment and opportunity for all persons without regard for race, creed, or color, or national origin, swept from the generals down to the GI's— Northerners and Southerners.

"The wars of this country," a Southern Senator said, "have been won by the white soldiers. Negro soldiers have rendered their greatest service as cooks, drivers and mechanics—"

Another Southern Senator, Strom Thurmond, said, "This is another effort on the part of the President to dominate this country by force . . . to put into effect these damnable proposals he has recommended under the guise of so-called civil rights."

Truman's position was simple and clear. He said he believed it had taken too long since the Emancipation Proclamation for America to implement all the civil rights people are entitled to under the Constitution.

"But," he added, "I firmly believe that it is coming, and I firmly believe it will come in our lifetime."

Now there appeared on the American scene, in the halls of Congress, a curious man, Senator Joseph McCarthy of Wisconsin, who gave form to a method of "investigation" which became known as McCarthyism.

Under McCarthyism, men and women were accused but not permitted to face their accusers. It was condemnation by innuendo, fear, brainwashing. It aroused the man from Missouri to anger.

"Many generations had fled to his country," he said, "to get away from *oppression by their own governments*. And it has always troubled me how some who called themselves Americans could themselves become oppressors." This was a clear reference to Senator McCarthy and this method of investigation.

One of the most important guarantees under the Bill of Rights is the right to claim exemption from self-incrimination. McCarthy made it appear that every witness who claimed this right was guilty.

"In the police state," Truman said angrily, "no individual has any immunity from persecution . . . In this country every person is protected against persecution by the Bill of Rights."

Under McCarthyism, hearsay evidence was frequently accepted as the truth. The government employee under "investigation" was smeared in such a way that he had no way of defending himself.

"This is what the Communists do," Truman asserted. "This is what McCarthy did, what the so-called Un-American Activities Committee in the House did. It simply cannot be squared with the Bill of Rights."

This had always been Truman's gauge when it came to civil liberties: "Can it be squared with the Bill of Rights?—the right of free speech and free assembly guaranteed to the American people in the Constitution."

Truman was concerned by the fact that while we seemed to be countering Communism around the world with firmness and effectiveness, at home we were in danger of losing these very liberties which had been threatened in Europe.

"Self-appointed guardians" of the country sprang up, attacking our schools and colleges.

"I do not believe," Truman said flatly, "that school teachers should be required to take a special oath. It is wrong to tell teachers not to discuss or not to teach subject matter that *should* be taught in a free education system. In education we must not limit the opportunities for generating ideas. There is no limit to knowledge. A person learns as long as he lives."

This is a forthright statement of a mind that is crystal clear about the quality of freedom and education in the great American tradition. While he fought to maintain freedom and democracy abroad, Harry Truman had to fight the bigots at home. He believed that if we cannot have confidence in our neighbors and the men and women who are teaching our children, "then our country is in trouble. Everyone," he declared, "has the right to express what he thinks. That, of course, lets the crackpots in. But if you cannot tell a crackpot when you see one, then you ought to be taken in."

Again, it was this direct, unadorned small-town approach to large issues that distinguished Truman not only as President but as a man. His domestic philosophy is stated in the simplest terms: "From 1930 to 1953 we had the greatest social and economic revolution in our history without violence. This was done in an orderly manner under the Constitution by the majority of the people, through the ballot, without curtailing the rights of individuals." Then the former dirt farmer, country supervisor, and haberdasher says: "Of course this great social change did not please some people, especially those who would like to see in this country a higher class and a lower class of society. But the everyday man today has more of the better things of life, the country is better off, and anyway, the people will not stand for being divided into classes." This is the judgment of a man of the people, the judgment of an uncomplicated man who has lived his family code: "To do the right thing, to do it the best we could, never complain, and never take advantage."

Harry S Truman is the ordinary man, EVERYMAN, in fact. He is so ordinary that in July 1948, when he went to the Capitol, Margaret reports, "a policeman on duty didn't recognize Dad and wouldn't let his driver park. 'Just move over,' the policeman said. Dad leaned out . . . and grinned. The policeman nearly fainted."

"Dear Mary," Truman wrote to his sister on the eve of Japan's surrender, "This is your birthday and I had intended to have a letter there this morning. Margaret should be out with some presents . . . I have a beautiful Belgian luncheon set for Mama and some handkerchiefs for Luella and a Swiss watch for Martha Ann . . . There hasn't been a minute . . . the Russian entry into the war, the Jap surrender offer and the usual business of the President's office have kept me busy night and day.

"It seems that things are going all right. Nearly every crisis seems to be the worst one, but after it's over, it isn't so bad . . .

"Happy birthday and lots of love,

Harry"

The Japanese surrender took place, at Truman's request, on board a naval vessel which had been christened by his daughter Margaret and which was named after his own state.

"My fellow Americans," the President said over the radio, "the thoughts and hopes of all America—indeed, of all the civilized world—are centered tonight on the battleship *Missouri*. There on that small piece of American soil anchored in Tokyo Harbor the Japanese have just officially laid down their arms . . . We think of our departed gallant leader,

Franklin D. Roosevelt, defender of democracy, architect of world peace and cooperation . . . From this day we move forward . . . With the other United Nations we move toward a new and better world of peace and international good will and cooperation."

Yet, within a few years, as had happened in Berlin, Russia and the United Nations were to confront each other in a military posture, and in this instance it led to war.

At the conference in Potsdam, it had been accepted that Korea, then under Japanese domination, would be divided at the 38th parallel after Japan was defeated. The Russians would administer the zone above the 38th parallel—North Korea—and American forces would occupy the southern zone.

A few weeks after the impressive ceremony of surrender on board the *Missouri,* the pattern of the Berlin crisis was established in Korea. By the spring of 1948 the situation in Korea was as tense as the situation in Berlin.

"We knew that this was one of the places where the Soviet-controlled Communist world might choose to attack," said Truman. But the same warlike atmosphere existed wherever Russian and American forces made contact, from Norway to Greece, from Iran to Malaya. The Soviet Union was forever probing the power and intentions of their former allies.

On Saturday, June 24, 1950, the President was spending the weekend in his home town, Independence, with his family. The telephone rang a little after ten o'clock in the library of the Truman house on North Delaware Street. The

President answered the phone. It was Secretary of State Dean Acheson, who said: "Mr. President, I have very serious news. The North Koreans have invaded South Korea."

Truman ordered Acheson to call an immediate session of the Security Council of the United Nations, while he himself flew back to the capital. He had many thoughts during that momentous flight. He remembered that each time the democracies failed to act, it had encouraged the aggressors. There was Manchuria, Ethiopia, Austria—all witnesses to this fact. Now, in Korea, Communism was behaving, he thought, just as Hitler, Mussolini, and the Japanese had behaved in the previous decades.

"If the Communists were permitted to force their way into the Republic of Korea without opposition from the free world, no small nation would have the courage to resist threats and aggression by stronger Communist neighbors. If this was allowed to go unchallenged it would mean a third world war." His thoughts were simply a restatement of the Truman Doctrine.

When he arrived in Washington, the President immediately conferred with his advisers. He was convinced that if the United Nations called for an immediate cease fire in Korea, the North Koreans would ignore the call, and he said so. General Omar Bradley said, "We would have to draw the line somewhere." Russia, he thought, was not yet ready for a new war, "but in Korea they were obviously testing us, and the line ought to be drawn now."

The President agreed with him emphatically. He expressed the opinion that the Russians were trying to get Korea by default, "gambling that we would be afraid of starting a third world war and would offer no resistance."

In a few days the news from Korea was dark and ominous. The troops of the South Koreans were no match for the mechanized weapons of the North Koreans. There was no doubt that if the Republic of Korea was to exist at all, it needed help at once. If the Communists succeeded in conquering all of Korea, it would put them within easy striking distance of Japan, of Okinawa and Formosa.

The President called General Douglas MacArthur on the telephone, and in person gave him his instructions. He was to support the forces of the Republic of Korea, but he was to remain south of the 38th parallel.

What was significant and new about the situation in Korea was that members of the United Nations sent troops to join the Americans under the blue flag of the U.N. "For the first time in history, men of many nations are fighting under a single banner to uphold the rule of law in the world," Truman announced in a broadcast on September 1. And then he listed the aims and intentions of his government's policy.

1. We believe in the United Nations and pledge ourselves to seek peace and security through that organization.

2. We believe that Koreans have a right to be free, independent and united.

3. We do not want the fighting in Korea to spread into a gen-

eral war; it will not spread unless Communist imperialism draws other armies and governments into the fight of the aggressors against the United Nations.

4. We hope in particular that the people of China will not be misled or forced into fighting against the United Nations and against the American people, who have always been and still are their friends.

5. We do not want Formosa or any part of Asia for ourselves.

6. We believe in freedom for all of the nations of the Far East.

7. We do not believe in aggressive or in preventive war.

8. Our men are fighting for peace today in Korea; we are working constantly for peace in the United Nations and in all the capitals of the world.

These eight points, stated by President Truman about the Korean War, could be restated meaningfully today about the conflict in Vietnam. Truman's aims and ideas have been woven into the very fabric of American domestic and foreign policy.

The fighting in Korea was bloody and fierce. Resistance was fanatical. But under the direction of General Douglas MacArthur the United Nations forces slowly pushed the North Koreans back behind the 38th parallel.

On October 2, MacArthur announced that army units of the Republic of Korea were operating north of the 38th parallel. Now Chou En-lai, the Foreign Minister of Communist China, proclaimed that if United Nations forces crossed the 38th parallel, China would send troops to help the North Koreans. If only South Korean troops crossed the 38th parallel, however, Chinese troops would *not* be ordered into action.

It had been President Truman's policy and the policy of his National Security Council not to risk a general war if it could possibly be avoided. Now the situation became complicated. The popular General MacArthur, ruler of 83,000,-000 defeated Japanese, Chief of the United Nations forces in Korea, the idol of millions who had fought in the Pacific War, and the friend of some of America's most powerful political figures, decided to back Chiang Kai-shek in a dangerous and reckless ambition. Chiang had been master of China until he and his regime were thrown out. He had then been forced to retreat to the island of Formosa. But he lay in wait for the moment when he could reconquer the Chinese mainland. Obviously, he couldn't fulfill his ambition without American armed forces.

"Chiang had nothing to lose by all-out war in Asia," Truman said. "Our position was more complicated. We were using our troops mainly to keep the Russians from taking over any more European countries. And if we invaded Red China, Russia then might very well come in to help them—building up to World War III."

The United States had entered the war in Korea to resist Soviet aggression, not to embark on a crusade for Chiang Kai-shek to regain his homeland. Truman sent Averell Harriman immediately to see MacArthur and to express the President's concern. Harriman came back to tell the President that the General didn't like to let down his old friend Chiang Kai-shek, but nevertheless he would "go along like a good soldier."

"Just what MacArthur meant by 'good soldier' became clear a few weeks later," Truman reports. "I was hopping mad."

MacArthur, in an article in *Life* magazine, called for a policy of military aggression that echoed Chiang Kai-shek's position. The tone of the article, which was a reprint of a message MacArthur had sent to a convention of the Veterans of Foreign Wars, was critical of President Truman's policy in Korea, critical of the policies of the National Security Council and of the U.N.

"My instinct," the President said, "was to replace MacArthur at once with Omar Bradley." But the President had more than his anger to consider. He had to consider the morale of the troops and of the United Nations. Dismissal would not only cause confusion but might be detrimental to the war effort.

"So I bottled up my anger and held off," Truman said. Now, as U.N. forces were crossing the 38th parallel and waging the war in North Korea, the President thought he had to talk face to face with MacArthur.

"If the mountain would not come to Washington," Truman says (he had wanted the General back home ever since the end of World War II, but MacArthur always had some excuse to stay where he was), "the government would come to him."

The President flew 7,600 miles to meet General MacArthur on Wake Island. The General traveled 2,000 miles. "And," Truman recalls, "the meeting was cordial—although the General did not salute his Commander-in-Chief." Then Truman continues in his simple, folksy way: "I brought a plum cake for Mrs. MacArthur."

The President and his general sat down to confer. The General was apologetic for any friction between them. He said he was sorry if his statement to the Veterans of Foreign Wars had caused Mr. Truman any embarrassment. He said that fighting in both North and South Korea would end by Thanksgiving. He was convinced that the Chinese Communists would not enter the war.

"Ten days later, the first Red Chinese patrols were captured in Korea. And ten days after that, the avalanche struck," Truman remembers. "Two hundred thousand Chinese Communist troops poured across the Yalu River from Manchuria, driving the U.N. forces back. And," he adds, "we were in the grease then sure enough.

"They gave us one heck of a shellacking in Korea. They pushed the United Nations forces right back to the 38th parallel again. We didn't even know whether we could hold there. The threat of World War III made people in America and Europe shiver in their boots."

Truman puts the situation in startling, clear, and colorful language: "That's when General MacArthur and I met head-on like two bull moose on mating day."

MacArthur wanted to bomb the supply lines of the Chinese Communists. He proposed an attack on the bridges over the Yalu River and the bombing of supply depots and plants behind the Chinese border. He also wanted permission to let Allied fighter planes go in pursuit of the Chinese jets, crossing into Chinese territory if necessary.

"Well, his plans made sense except for one thing," Truman says. That one thing happened to be the fact that Russia and China were allies, not only ideologically, but by treaty. Russia would surely be called upon to come to the aid of her Chinese ally.

"I felt that we were sure to trigger World War III as soon as we attacked Red China herself," says Truman. "Now, who was to make the final decision?"

MacArthur insisted we bomb Red China. "I told him that he was concerned with only some part of the battle with Communism. But I had the whole of Europe and the world to worry about. I told him no dice." This is how President Truman recalls this tense moment, but the official records reveal caution tempered with firmness in his orders to MacArthur:

"You are authorized to go ahead with your planned bombing in *Korea near the frontier* including [the] Korean end of Yalu bridges . . . The above does *not* authorize the bombing of any dams or power plants on the Yalu River . . . Because it is vital in the national interests of the U.S. to *localize the fighting in Korea* it is important that extreme care be taken to avoid violation of Manchurian territory and airspace."

MacArthur's reply came in a letter to Joe Martin, Minority Leader in the House and a man who often severely criticized the President. Martin made the MacArthur letter public. It was a slap at Truman and his policy of containing the war in Korea.

"It seems strangely difficult for some to realize that here in Asia . . ." MacArthur said, "is where we fight Europe's war with arms while the diplomats there still fight with words."

"This," says Truman, "was a flat challenge to presidential authority." Senator Kilgore reported that Truman was beside himself with fury, that he exploded, "I'll show him who's boss, and who does he think he is—God?"

Truman had meeting after meeting with his advisers. Something had to be done with a general who disagreed with the policies laid down by his government and who refused to carry them out. General George Marshall studied all the correspondence between the Joint Chiefs of Staff and the Far East Commander, General MacArthur. When he had completed his study, "he came into my office," Truman recalls, "and I'd never seen him so mad. He hadn't taken two steps into the room before he said, 'You should have fired the so-and-so two years ago.'" Then Truman adds, "Only he didn't say the so-and-so."

The issue was now joined. And the issue was larger than the seeming insubordination of an officer to his Commander-in-Chief. A principle of American democracy was at stake. Truman puts it succinctly:

"I have always believed that civilian control of the military is one of the strongest foundations of our system of free government. Many of our people are descended from men and women who fled their native countries to escape the oppression of militarism . . . we have always jealously guarded the constitutional provision that prevents the military from taking over the government from the authorities, elected by the people, in whom the power resides."

Truman then goes on to contrast the mentality of the elected official and that of the military officer. He maintains that success for the elected man is a mixture of principles "steadfastly maintained and adjustments made at the proper time and place—adjustments to *conditions,* not adjustments of principles."

The military officer, on the other hand, is raised on such words as "command" and "obedience"—and the military definitions "of those words *are not definitions for use in a republic."*

Truman pinpoints the problem. "That is why," he contends, "our Constitution embodies the principle of civilian control of the military. This was the principle that General MacArthur threatened."

On April 11, at one o'clock in the morning, reporters were handed the statement announcing that President Truman had relieved General MacArthur of his command.

"General MacArthur's place in history as one of our greatest commanders is fully established. The Nation owes him a debt of gratitude for the distinguished and exceptional service which he has rendered his country in posts of great responsibility." This was Truman's gracious farewell to his general.

The dismissal of MacArthur was an act of courage, no matter how one views the problem. MacArthur had powerful friends in government, business, and financial circles. He was the idol of millions of Americans.

"What I did was simply to uphold the office of the President," says Truman. This statement could very well have been emblazoned as his motto for the years he was in office.

# 14

There are many facets to the role Harry Truman played as President. It was he who first offered the secrets of making atomic energy to the United Nations, provided proper safeguards could be established against its use for destructive purposes. The most powerful nation in the world was willing to turn over its knowledge to an international body, for the good of all people, everywhere.

It was he who demanded that Nazi war criminals be given a "just, swift and *public* trial." Winston Churchill was opposed to any trial for the Nazi leaders. He wanted them shot immediately.

"But killing the war criminals without a trial was not my idea of justice," the new President had said. "That was revenge. I wanted them *tried*."

*The New York Times* said: "There is no need for a trial of a war criminal whose punishment has been previously determined."

The *St. Louis Post Dispatch* said: "Put them out of this world with army bullets through their heads."

But Truman insisted that the captured Nazis be given a fair trial. He told Anthony Eden, "You do what you want with the Nazis you have—and we will try the ones we grab—and history will decide who did the right thing."

Eden capitulated; France and Russia followed suit. And for the first time in history, it was an *international* tribunal which was the complainant, the conscience of mankind.

Justice was done. Posterity may forget the names of the criminals, but "that is not the point," says Truman. "We had no precedent to follow in the war trials—but we made one. We blazed a path for international law to follow in times to come. Never again can men say, 'I was only following orders.'" It was the simple democrat from Lamar, Grandview, and Independence, Missouri, who demanded justice for even the worst criminals the world has ever known.

It was Truman who, during his administration, ushered

into being the first of the new small nations to emerge out of Asia and Africa after World War II. That nation was Israel.

"The British," Truman said, "didn't really ever talk about creating a state or a commonwealth for the Jews—they kept talking about a 'center' for Jews, whatever that meant. I wanted to do something—because I figured History owed a homeland to what Jews were left after Hitler killed six million of them. But nobody would let me do it. The Arabs wanted the Jews out, the British wanted a status quo—the United States State Department and Chiefs of Staff didn't want to antagonize the Arabs—and the Jews didn't want any compromise—they wanted all Palestine free and clear. Well, what are you going to do in a fix like that?"

There is a touching story of how Eddie Jacobson, Truman's partner in the haberdashery business, came to see his old friend in the White House one day.

"He came in," Truman remembers, "tired and a little older-looking. And he just stood there at first; so quiet—my old friend Eddie Jacobson. You know, lots of people have asked me how come I went into business with a Jew. That's always annoyed me! Never meant a damn thing to me: a man's religion, a man's color—never will—and it's high time this kind of archaic thinking stopped for Americans. I went into business with a man, a human being—Eddie Jacobson.

"Well, there he just stood . . . my old friend . . . In all my years in politics, Eddie had never asked me for a single thing. Now he could hardly talk.

"I remember I walked to the window and looked out at the grass . . . the streets. Finally, after a long silence, I turned to him and said: 'Well, after thirty years you've finally come to ask for something?' "

Eddie Jacobson *did* come to ask for something after thirty years. He wanted his friend, now the President of the United States, to see Chaim Weizmann, an old man, who had traveled thousands of miles to talk with the President about recognizing the new State of Israel. Truman was meeting with opposition in every quarter on this matter. Nevertheless, "when Eddie left, I gave instructions to have Dr. Weizmann come to the White House as soon as it could be arranged. But—through a side door."

The future first President of the new state of Israel, Dr. Weizmann, was assured of Truman's support. On November 29, 1948, Truman wrote a letter to Weizmann which said, in part: ". . . We have already expressed our willingness to help develop the new State through financial and economic measures . . . I was pleased to learn that the first Israeli elections have been scheduled for January 25. That enables us to set a definite target for extending *de jure* recognition.

"In closing, I want to tell you how happy and impressed I have been at the remarkable progress made by the new State of Israel. What you have received at the hands of the world has been far less than was your due. But you have more than made the most of what you have received, and I admire you for it . . ."

The Israelis named a village after their friend Truman, and they wanted to erect a statue of him. This is what he said:

"I was very touched and grateful, and a little overwhelmed by the sense of immortality that seems to go with having a village named after you. But the statue? I dunno—statues are made for people like Andy Jackson or Abe Lincoln, or Chaim Weizmann. I'm not ready to be put into a statue yet."

For almost eight years, Harry S Truman held the destinies of millions of people in his hands. He made decisions that changed the course of history. And on March 4, 1953, he was no longer President. He was plain Mr. Citizen. He returned home to Independence to be greeted by the Mayor of the town and vast crowds.

"He'll always be Mr. President to us," the Mayor said. "He's home folks to us! We are glad to have all of you here to greet him tonight! Welcome home, neighbor!"

"Well, we're back home for good now," Mr. Citizen said in reply. "I'm here to tell you that when I get the job done that Mrs. Truman has for me . . . and she says that I have to unpack all our goods . . . it will take seven or eight men three months to get it done, so I don't know how long it's going to take one man to get it undone. After that, I will be open to dinner engagements, because I may be hungry by that time! We do thank you immensely for this wonderful welcome. I don't see how anyone in the world could have a better one. Thank you very much!"

Bess and Harry Truman moved their things back into their old home on North Delaware Street. Nearby, now, is the Truman Library, which houses three and a half million documents concerning one of the most vital periods in American history, over which the man from Independence had so much influence.

"I had hoped that after I left the White House, I would, in some way, find an opportunity to talk to young people about the operation of our government and the function and meaning of the Presidency. To me, there is nothing more rewarding than to stand before the school children who come here to the library and find them so vitally interested in everything pertaining to the affairs of the country and the world."

General Marshall once said of the man who made this statement about "the meaning and function of the Presidency":

"The full measure of this man will be proved only by history. But . . . there never has been a decision made under this man's Administration . . . that has not been made in the best interest of his country. It is *not only the courage of these decisions that will live, but the integrity of them.*"

It is Margaret Truman who perhaps best sums up the character of the thirty-third President of the United States:

"What can I say about my father that will make you see

him whole—except that *he cares*. He cares about everything, and nothing is too much trouble. His philosophies are singularly basic—the greatest good for the greatest number; the end can never justify the means; do as you would be done by; do the best you can; don't give up; don't be afraid."

Yes, there is a gravestone in Boothill Cemetery, Tombstone, Arizona. The epitaph reads: "Here lies Jack Williams. He done his damnedest. What more can a person do?"

# Bibliography

Acheson, Dean, *Sketches from Life of Men I Have Known*, 1961.

Byrnes, James F., *All in One Lifetime*, 1958.

———, *Speaking Frankly*, 1947.

Churchill, Sir Winston, *Second World War*, 1948–53.

Daniels, Jonathan, *The Man of Independence*, 1950.

Goldman, Eric, *The Crucial Decade*, 1956.

Ickes, Harold, *Secret Diary*, 1953–54.

Koenig, L., ed., *Truman Administration: Its Principles and Practices*, 1956.

McNaughton, Frank, and Walter Hehmeyer, *Harry Truman: President*, 1948.

Schauffler, E., *Harry Truman: Son of the Soil*, 1947.

Smith, Merriman, *Thank You, Mr. President,* 1946.
Steinberg, Alfred, *The Man from Missouri,* 1962.
Truman, Harry S, *Mr. Citizen,* 1960.
———, *Memoirs,* 1956.
Truman, Margaret (with Margaret Cousins), *Souvenir,* 1956.
Zornow, William F., *America at Mid-Century: The Truman Administration,* 1959.